CONCISE GUIDE TO BIOMEDICAL POLYMERS
Their Design Fabrication + Molding

John W. Boretos

Concise Guide to
Biomedical Polymers

With Forewords by

William S. Pierce, M.D.

Assistant Professor
Cardiovascular and Thoracic Surgery
Department of Surgery
The Milton S. Hershey Medical Center
Pennsylvania State University
Hershey, Pennsylvania

and

Silas Braley

Director
Center for Aid to Medical Research
Dow Corning Corporation
Midland, Michigan

Concise Guide to Biomedical Polymers

Their Design, Fabrication and Molding

By

JOHN W. BORETOS

Biomedical Engineering and Instrumentation Branch
Division of Research Services
National Institutes of Health
Department of Health, Education, and Welfare
Bethesda, Maryland

CHARLES C THOMAS · PUBLISHER
Springfield · Illinois · U.S.A.

CHEMISTRY

Published and Distributed Throughout the World by
CHARLES C THOMAS • PUBLISHER
BANNERSTONE HOUSE
301–327 East Lawrence Avenue, Springfield, Illinois, U.S.A.

© *1973, by* CHARLES C THOMAS • PUBLISHER
ISBN 0–398–026674–2
Library of Congress Catalog Card Number: 72–88441

With THOMAS BOOKS *careful attention is given to all details of
manufacturing and design. It is the Publisher's desire to present books
that are satisfactory as to their physical qualities and artistic possibilities
and appropriate for their particular use.* THOMAS BOOKS *will be true
to those laws of quality that assure a good name and good will.*

Printed in the United States of America
K–8

—————————————————————————————Foreword

THE SUCCESSFUL USE of implantable prostheses, such as ven-
triculojugular shunts, prosthetic cardiac valves, implantable
pacemakers and orthopedic prostheses, has improved the length
and quality of life for a significant number of people. The availability of these devices is the result of the dynamic integration of a
thorough understanding of the basic biological problem, an idea
for an approach to the solution and the ability to translate that
idea into a useful, implantable prosthesis.

Many areas of biomedical research are dedicated to the development of implantable devices, the functions of which are
limited only by the imagination. Researchers who work in these
areas must have special knowledge and facilities that will enable
translation of their ideas into working devices. Success in this
field requires knowledge of materials and fabrication procedures
and facilities just as much as productive cancer research requires a knowledge of intermediary metabolism and a chemistry
laboratory.

The search for special biocompatible materials continues at
an ever-increasing pace, but investigators continue to disagree on
exactly what is meant by "biocompatible." There is no question
that certain rigid and elastomeric materials evoke less tissue
reaction than do others and that certain materials, when implanted in the vascular system, are less likely to induce thrombus
formation than are others. Indeed, a wider selection of materials
is available each year that are less reactive or less thrombogenic
than previously.

The problems of fabricating *useful* implantable devices, however well tolerated by the host, involves more than just materials.
The device must employ a design which operates within the
limits of the mechanical properties of those materials and which

v

performs the required biological function. The device must be fabricated properly, for a poor surface finish or an abrasive, imbedded in a soft polymer during the final polishing phase, may well cause ultimate failure of the device in a biological system, no matter what material is used. A similar statement may be made concerning proper cleanliness of the implanted device. An oily fingerprint or powder from the surgeon's glove may serve as a nidus for thrombus formation in a vascular prosthesis. These facts seem apparent, yet many new medical devices fabricated for implantation continue to fail, not because of the unavailability of biocompatible material but because of improper design, fabrication techniques or implantation procedure.

The biological organism remains a very stern and intolerant judge and each aspect of an implantable device must be designed and fabricated with its ultimate use in mind, or failure will occur. Thus, outwitting the biological organism by developing an acceptable prosthetic "part," be it a prosthetic joint or an artificial heart, remains the true challenge to all interested in this field.

This book that John Boretos has prepared fulfills a definite need for those interested in biomedical prostheses and for those responsible for the fabrication of such devices. The manuscript represents the experience of a man who has spent his professional life directing the fabrication of biomedical devices and constantly seeking improved biocompatible materials and methods for their fabrication. It is a practical book and one in which the reader will find ideas applicable to future inquiry as well as answers to his present material and fabrication problems.

William S. Pierce

E VERY VOCATION, by its very nature, has developed its own lore, not only in substance but also in language. Modern technology is so immense that the age of the generalist is long past, and whether we are carpenters or chorus girls, policemen or polymer chemists, we know relatively little about the details of the specialties of others.

When we attempt to get some insight into these other worlds, we are confused by the volume of information and by the words spoken there: An otolaryngologist talking with an oculist would not be communicating when he says that the patient has a velopharyngeal insufficiency, nor is an architect understood by most of us when he refers to a quoin.

Interdisciplinary scientists, especially those working in both engineering and medicine, find themselves enmeshed in these difficulties.

Fortunately for the engineer, there are medical dictionaries, and the problems of design for physiological purposes are not completely foreign to him: He simply has to change his framework of thought from the inaminate to the animate—and to remember that he cannot closely control nor accurately measure his conditions, nor his subject, as he customarily does when he plans a water system or a plastic toy.

But the physician has not had these advantages. When he wants to build a "plastic" device to use in his studies, he has usually had to do it by himself by means of what bits and pieces of isolated information he could find. He knows of the existence of polymers that perhaps could be used as construction materials for his device, but he knows little about how or whether they can be fabricated into something he can use safely. When he goes to a library for help, he finds that the few texts written in the field of plastics fabrication are usually designed to be read by persons who already have experience in the field and its language. In addition, these texts are usually fragmented so that a book on rubber fabrication is no help in handling Teflon® or Plexiglas®.

There are several excellent texts designed to acquaint the nonchemist with the nature of the various polymers and to explain where they have been used in various physiological applications. But until now there has been little to help the uninitiated decide which polymer can most readily be fabricated and then to tell him how to fabricate it into a given device.

Mr. Borotos' book is designed to fill this gap, and does so admirably.

From it, the physician-designer can now find which of the many polymers available have the properties he needs and how they can most readily be fabricated into his design. He can learn about gluing and dipping techniques, mold making and milling, calendering and extrusion, and a host of other polymer fabrication techniques. He can learn what these polymers are chemically and where to obtain them. The listing of the trade names and sources of polymers alone will be of great value to all of us in the medical device field.

The last thirty years has seen enormous growth in the technology of polymers, but their application to the biomedical field is only just beginning. Mr. Boretos has made a great contribution to biomedical engineering knowledge.

SILAS BRADLEY

PLASTIC AND RUBBER, in some form, have been part of surgical paraphernalia for decades. Items such as breathing devices, electrical insulators or rubber gloves, although commonplace, are essential to safe practice.

The use of polymers as implants is a recent innovation that has grown slowly but steadily.

In a review article in 1947 (1), only three commercially available plastics and one rubber were cited as promising for surgical implants. Skull defects and hip injuries were being repaired with polymethyl methacrylate; polyethylene showed short-term biological inertness and was being investigated; and nylon was a popular suture material. A few attempts had been made at using natural rubber but it was limited mostly to catheters. Silicone rubber was still untested.

Since this modest beginning, almost every conceivable polymer, and many specially tailored variations, have been applied to the repair or replacement of the heart, lungs, kidney, brain, bones and tissues. Two publications (2, 3) have reported the use of fifteen different polymers in one application. Today, the value of implantable prostheses made from polymers is clearly established; mainly through the efforts of universities, government laboratories, private institutes, polymer synthesizers and medical products manufacturers. Doubtless, this technology will continue to grow as an essential part of biomedical research and the practice of clinical medicine.

Because of their versatility, polymers have captured the imaginations of the inventor, designer, developer and user. They can be simultaneously strong, light, porous or nonporous, flexible or rigid. Modifications can produce unique physical and chemical properties necessary for specific applications. As a result, new materials are constantly being developed; with each polymer comes a completely different set of properties and fabrication techniques.

No polymer is completely inert. The extent to which they become altered or interact unfavorably depends upon the location in the body; the physical, chemical and electrical stresses to which they are subject; and the duration of implantation. Implicated in the *in vivo* breakdown of properties are changes in cross-linking, oxidative or hydrolytic degradation, phase changes and absorption of body fluids. These alterations can result in loss of strength, change in permeability, embrittlement, stress cracking and changes in elastic modulus.

Difficulties often arise from processing variations. The generic name given to specific polymers does not necessarily imply possible differences in crystallinity, molecular weight, chain branching, cross-linking or presence of end groups of the same named material from batch to batch or from the generic equivalent from one or more manufacturers. What, therefore, is often believed to be a replication of previous experience is, in fact, a manifestation of unrecognized conditions which foster inconsistent performance.

Potential irritability to tissues is an important consideration in acute or chronic applications. Some materials may function satisfactorily for a few days or weeks before chemical or physical interactions induce inflammation or rejection. Partially reacted or incompletely cured plastics and rubbers invariably evoke biological response.

Devices placed in the bloodstream generate fixed thrombi and small clots which are transported throughout the vascular system. To retard thrombus formation, surfaces must be smooth and clean, and the configuration must avoid contours which encourage stasis, stagnation or turbulence. Gott and Akira (4) have categorized seventeen biomaterials as having thrombo-resistant properties as evaluated using the vena cava ring test (*see* special materials, Ch. I).

Adverse reactions can be generated by physical or mechanical shortcomings. Shape, size and weight depend crucially upon the particular site selected for the implant. Tissues, nerves and blood vessels are easily damaged by undue force or pressure exerted by an instrument, sharp corners, protrusions or abrasive surfaces. Erosion through the skin has been observed as a result of improperly secured implants and care must be exercised, when closing the tissues over the implant, to avoid dead space which can permit migration of the device or can provide conditions for infection to occur.

Table 1 categorizes those polymers most commonly used as implants in general order of stability.

TABLE 1

IN VIVO STABILITY OF POLYMERS *

(Most Commonly Used Biomaterials)

Stable

Dacron	Polypropylene
Polyethylene, high density	Silicone rubber
Polyether urethanes	Teflon

Semistable

Chlorosulfonated polyethylene	Polycarbonate
Epichlorohydrin	Polyethylene, medium density
Natural rubber	Polymethyl methacrylate
Nylon	

Unstable

Acrylate rubber	Polyvinyl alcohol
Polyester urethane	Polyvinyl chloride
Polyethylene, low density	

* Exact order is dependent upon conditions of use.

The ability to produce innovative and high-quality devices requires, therefore, a thorough knowledge of not only the functional characteristics and limitations of these materials but of the techniques involved in the proper execution of their joining, machining and molding.

A staff for a comprehensive biomedical materials laboratory capable of controlling these variables might consist of seven, distributed as follows: a chemist or chemical engineer, a mechanical engineer, three technicians and two machinists. The chemist or chemical engineer, experienced in materials science, could judge how best to tailor polymers to meet specific sets of conditions or develop entirely new materials. The mechanical engineer would serve to transform these polymers into functional form by applying an understanding of materials handling characteristics, design, theory, methods, analysis and so forth. A technician, with dental prosthetics or plastics molding background, could form and cast intricate shapes. Finally, the staff should include two technicians with a working knowledge of chemical procedures and physical test methods and two machinists for fabricating device parts and molds. Such a team should be well equipped to transform imaginative design into reality on a routine basis.

For the small facility with limited funds, however, responsibility for a complete system may be relegated to a few medical or paramedical personnel. The purpose of this monograph, therefore, is to arrange in one source many of these properties and techniques as a helpful guide to the physician, biomedical engineer or laboratory technician engaged in this new and rapidly expanding field of artificial organs. Sections of this book deal with industrial polymers and processes, many of which form the basis of much of the current work with biomedical plastics, while other parts contain special materials and highly specialized techniques which have been experimentally and empirically derived by other medical research teams.

A number of physical properties of biomedical polymers will be compared in an attempt to characterize their capabilities; to add perspective, an appendix outlines properties of hard and soft body tissues. Many technical terms or abbreviations commonly used to describe polymers and their design, molding and fabricating are defined in the glossary along with the names and addresses of current sources of supply. Let us consider these materials and how they may be used.

REFERENCES

1. Ingraham, F.D., Alexander, E., and Martson, D.D.: Medical progress: Synthetic plastic materials in surgery. *Engl J Med, 236*:362, 1947.
2. Meredino, K.A.: *Prosthetic Valves for Cardiac Surgery.* Springfield, Charles C Thomas, 1961.
3. Brewer, L.A.: *Prosthetic Heart Valves.* Springfield, Charles C Thomas, 1969.
4. Gott, V.L., and Akira, F.: Antithrombogenic surfaces, classification and *in vivo* evaluation. *Fed Proc, 30*:1679–1685, 1971.

Acknowledgments

I wish to thank the many individuals and companies whose works are cited in this monograph. Also, I wish to express my appreciation to Dr. Robert Dedrick and Dr. Lester Goodman, for their engineering advice and encouragement; to Dr. Nina S. Braunwald, Dr. Ayub K. Ommaya and Dr. William S. Pierce, for invaluable clinical experience, and to Mr. James H. Donachy, for many years of assistance.

Special thanks and credit go to my wife, Nancy, for help that made this book possible.

J.W.B.

Figures

Tables

Contents

Concise Guide to
Biomedical Polymers

I

Biomedical Polymers

Biomedical polymers, in the form of rubber and plastic, have progressed rapidly in use from their initial role as low-cost manufacturer's substitutes to their present position as materials of choice for heart valves, heart-lung devices, catheters, pacemakers, cranioplastic prostheses, joint implants, dental appliances and others. This progression has resulted from the fact that polymers have combinations of properties not common to other materials and are readily tailored to meet specific needs.

Rubber and plastic will be treated separately giving appropriate examples; special surfaces, fabrics and sutures will also be discussed in relationship to biomedical prostheses.

ELASTOMERS

Elastomers (that is, rubber) * are polymers of entangled long-chain molecules capable of large and reversible deformations. They possess a broad range of chemical, electrical and physical characteristics; inherent noise and vibration damping; and energy storage and absorption properties. These molecular units have mobile side groups which are permanently joined, or cross-linked, when vulcanized. As stress is applied, from an imposed load, some molecules align themselves in the direction of stress and unwind to resist deformation. The cross-linked structure serves as a limit to elongation and encourages the rubber to return to its original configuration. Energy is produced

* Note that a number of rigid plastics are suitable for implantation, whereas only polyether urethane and Silastic® are appropriate for long-term use in the body.

3

as heat with stretching and the ability of an elastomer to absorb large amounts of this energy, without permanently effecting its shape, differentiates it from other long-chain polymers such as polyethylene.

Performance of artificial hearts, blood oxygenators, cannulas, catheters, prosthetic heart valves, subcutaneous implants, cosmetic appliances and vascular replacements often depend on the elastomeric characteristics of materials. No single rubber

TABLE 2

COMPARATIVE PROPERTIES OF ELASTOMERIC COMPOUNDS * (1)

Polymer	Tensile Strength (psi)	Ultimate Elongation (%)	Specific Gravity †	Durometer Hardness, Shore A	Temperature Limits (F)
Acrylate	1000–2200	100–400	1.10	40–100	0 to 300
Butyl	1000–3000	100–700	0.92	30–100	−65 to 212
Epichlorohydrin	1000–2500	100–400	1.27	60–90	−50 to 250
Fluroelastomers	1000–2400	100–350	1.4 −1.95	60–90	−40 to 450
Hypalon	1000–2800	100–500	1.10	50–95	−65 to 250
Natural rubber	1000–4000	100–700	0.93	20–100	−65 to 180
Polysulfide	500–1250	100–400	1.34	20–80	−65 to 180
Silicone	500–1500	50–800	0.98	20–95	−120 to 450
Urethane	1000–8000	100–700	0.85–1.1	55–95	−65 to 300

* See specific polymer.
† Uncompounded, g/cc.

possesses ideal properties for all conditions of use, therefore a variety of materials must be available to solve design problems. Those most commonly applied to medical implants will be described; many others hold potentials still unexplored. Typical properties of several elastomers are compared in Table 2 to show physical differences that exist.

Acrylate Elastomers

Leonard and co-workers (2) developed a saturated acrylate elastomeric latex with desirable properties for maxillofacial and orthotic prostheses. The basic polymer latex is prepared by emulsion polymerization of butyl acrylate, methyl methacrylate and methacrylamide (all three from Rohm & Haas Co.). Once the latex is prepared, the following additional ingredients are added to produce rubber items:

Acrylate terpolymer latex	100 pbw *
(Polyscience Inc.)	
Polyethylenemethacrylate	37 pbw
(Rohm & Haas Co.)	
Formaline	1.765 pbw

Rubber coverings of artificial limbs and arms for amputees can be made, duplicating exact contours, by employing the dipping process. (*See* dipping and gypsum, Ch. IV.) Reinforcement with cloth such as Dacron® is usually necessary because of the polymer's inherent weakness.

Thromboresistance can be achieved by adding an anionic surfactant to the recipe. Vascular grafts made from this material seemed promising at first, but according to Leonard, "loss of flexibility developed over several months when implanted in experimental animals."

Byck and co-workers (3) have experimented with an ethylene/acrylate copolymer and its ionomers in attempts to produce a blood compatible polymer. Although some promising results have come out of this work, the polymer is yet in the developmental stage.

Butyl Rubber

Butyl rubber is a long-chain saturated hydrocarbon elastomer made from isobutylene with small amounts of isoprene. The polymer is important for its low gas permeability; high ozone and chemical resistance; shock and vibration absorption; and high flex-life in dynamic applications. Although no direct implantable use of this elastomer can be cited, it has found widespread use in paramedical application. For example, butyl rubber without carbon black filler is used in the pharmaceutical industry for self-sealing stoppers which must be chemically inert and retain their integrity after repeated punctures. (*See* Table 3.)

Chlorosulfonated Polyethylene (Hypalon®)

Hypalon (E.I. du Pont de Nemours Co., Inc.) synthetic rubber is available in several commercial types, all based on the

* pbw = parts by weight. See glossary for abbreviations, definitions and addresses.

TABLE 3

TYPICAL FORMULATION FOR PUNCTURE-RESISTANT
BUTYL RUBBER (4)

Material	pbw
Enjay butyl 365 *	100
Zinc oxide	5
Platy talcum	20–30
Calcined kaolin	30–20
TMTDS †	1.0
MBT ‡	0.5
Diethylene glycol	2.0
Sulfur	1.25

Cure: 30 minutes @ 320 F

* Enjay Chemical Co.
† TMTDS = Tetramethylthiuram disulfide
‡ MBT = Mercaptobenzothiazole, R. T.
Vanderbilt Co., Inc.
Note: Not intended for implants.

polymer chlorosulfonated polyethylene. Outstanding properties offered by this elastomer are resistance to aging at elevated temperatures, food color stability, high ozone and chemical resistance.

Wright and associates (5) observed chlorosulfonated polyethylene to be well tolerated within the canine bloodstream for short periods and to significantly resist blood clotting even without heparination. Although this work was reported in 1966, it has not been pursued by others.

Hypalon can be vulcanized by means of litharge,

TABLE 4

TYPICAL COMPOSITION OF HYPALON RUBBER USED
FOR FOOD HANDLING (6)

Material	pbw
Hypalon 20 *	100
Hydrogenated wood rosin †	2.5
Magnesia	20.0
Hard clay	50.0
Titanium dioxide	10.0
Heavy paraffin oil ‡	10.0
Tetrone A §	1.0

Press cure: 30 minutes at 307 F.
* E.I. du Pont de Nemours and Co., Inc.
† Staybelite resin, Hercules Powder Co.
‡ Fractol A, Esso Standard Oil Co.
§ Dipentamethylene-thiuram-tetrasulfide, E.I. du
Pont de Nemours and Co., Inc.
Note: Food handling materials are not necessarily acceptable for implants.

litharge/magnesia, or magnesia systems; the latter being most favorable where a nontoxic rubber is required. Food-processing conveyor belt covers have been made from Hypalon and are resistant to edible fats and oils, air and indirect sunlight, and do not contain ingredients which can effect the taste or quality of foods they contact. Table 4 gives the composition of Hypalon approved for food handling.

Epichlorohydrin (Hydrin®) Rubber

There are two basic types of Hydrin rubber (B.F. Goodrich Co.): (a) Hydrin 100® which is a polymer made from epichlorohydrin and (b) Hydrin 200® which is a copolymer of epichlorohydrin and ethylene oxide.

TABLE 5

TYPICAL FORMULATION FOR MOLDING HYDRIN RUBBER (7)

Material	pbw
Hydrin 200 *	100
Cab-O-Sil †	25
Hexamethylene diamine	3

Cure: 45 minutes @ 310 F.

* B.F. Goodrich Co.
† Godfrey L. Cabot, Inc.
Note: Not intended for implants.

Hydrin 100 is three times as impermeable to gases as butyl rubber and has high ozone, solvent, fuel and oil resistance. Unlike butyl rubber, Hydrin 100 is self-extinguishing.

Hydrin 200 is a highly resilient elastomer which can be vulcanized by diamine curing systems. (*See* Table 5.)

Grode and co-workers (8) have data demonstrating that Hydrin compounds can be rendered nonthrombogenic by curing with various diamines, then exposing the cured product to a heparin solution.

Natural Rubber

Natural rubber is obtained directly from the Havea Brasiliensis tree as liquid latex. Commercially, the latex is available as solution or as dried sheets suitable for pressure molding. It can be compression molded in a metal mold at high temperatures and pressures, or it can be dipped from solution and vulcanized in hot air or water. (*See* pressure molding and dipping, Ch. IV.)

The original rubber compound as developed by Goodyear was

Natural rubber	100 pbw
Sulfur	5–10 pbw

Today's formulations offer greater properties. Additives are included to overcome inherent weaknesses, fillers such as carbon black and calcium carbonate are added to give rubber additional strength and various curing agents can reduce the time and temperature of molding.

The first synthetic vascular graft made from natural rubber latex was used by Horsley (9) in the early nineteen hundreds. However, very little interest was shown for the implantation of natural rubber for the next five decades. In 1963, Atsumi and co-workers (10) departed from the common sulfur vulcanization techniques and increased the tissue compatibility characteristics of natural rubber by cross-linking molecular chains with x-ray and organic peroxide systems. The physical properties of the resulting latex films differed from that obtained with natural rubber-sulfur systems; the tensile strength dropped and the elongation at break increased, along with an increase in tear resistance.

By removing the water-soluble (that is, protein, polysaccharides and inorganics) contaminating components from natural rubber latex, Nosé and associates (11) has reduced its tendencies to generate blood clots when implanted into the vascular system. Purification of the natural rubber is achieved by centrifuging dilute latex and further centrifugation of the cured rubber. He equates this specially treated rubber with the biocompatibility of silicone rubber. After treating, little *in vivo* difference can be observed between peroxide cured, purified sulfur cured or gamma irradiation cured natural rubber.

Weber and Imai (12,13) have removed many of the naturally occurring protein contaminates that have caused adverse tissue reactions and like Nosé have found that tissue compatibility is greatly improved by the double centrifuging technique. The purified rubber, according to Imai, has no adverse effect on its

TABLE 6

EFFECT OF RECENTRIFUGATION ON MECHANICAL
PROPERTIES OF NATURAL RUBBER (13)

Specimen	Type of Cure	Tensile Strength (psi)	Ultimate Elongation (%)
Control	gamma ray	3,060	960
	sulfur	3,510	880
Recentrifuged	gamma ray	2,920	990
	sulfur	3,920	840

mechanical properties. He has also shown that albumin treated with formaldehyde and mixed with natural rubber offers a degree of thromboresistance. Table 6 compares the properties of purified rubber and conventional natural rubber, both being made from latex and of the same relative composition.

Natural rubber has been employed in a number of unique applications. For example, Cook (14) has used a latex rubber balloon coated with a thermoplastic, resin-plasticizer mixture of polyvinyl butyral and alkyl aryl phosphate to obtain impressions of the human endometrium for diagnosis of cancer. The balloon is inserted in a collapsed configuration and then inflated by water pressure at 45 C; the heat transferred from the water softens the plastic. The balloon touches the walls of the endometrium at all points allowing tissue cells to be picked up on the surface of the balloon at the same time as an impression of the endometrium is formed by the soft plastic coating; contours and rough surfaces indicate an abnormal condition of the tissues. The water temperature is lowered to 40 C to solidify the coating and facilitate removal of the balloon without impairing the impression.

Balloons on the end of catheters are used to extract blood clots within vessels and the Swan-Ganz * catheter is light enough to float within the bloodstream to remote areas for intravascular measurements of pressure. Latex has been widely used for construction of artificial hearts and others.

Trans-1,4 polyisoprene

This easily shaped isomer of natural rubber is actually thermoplastic. The unfilled rubber is hard and semirigid at room temperature but becomes soft, self-adherent and easily shaped

---

* Edwards Laboratory.

at 160 to 180 F. Polysar X-414® (Polymer Corp. Limited) is a reinforced version of the basic polymer and is being used to immobilize injured parts of the body. Unlike plaster of Paris this material is light, tough, impermeable to water and easily maintained by the patient (15).

Polyurethanes

Polyester urethane has been described as having excellent flex-life and tensile properties, as resistant to gamma radiation, oils, strong acids and alkali, and causing minimal adverse tissue reactions. Mirkovitch and associates (16), however, have shown the Estane® (B.F. Goodrich, Co.) urethanes to degrade rapidly when implanted in the muscle of dogs or when used as monocusp valvular prostheses. Sharp and co-workers (17) have observed thromboresistance on a polyester polyether diamine cured polyurethane (R149X32-1 prepolymer and R149X32-4 amine curative, Goodyear Tire and Rubber Co.), which has been modified by the inclusion of ten parts carbon black per hundred parts of resin. The carbon is added to the urethane prepolymer by ball milling for seventy-two hours and the amine is added just prior to use. Articles are produced by dipping from a ketone solution of the polyurethane.

Boretos and Pierce (18) introduced the medical use of segmented polyurethane, a polyether elastomer, with monomer chains of hard segments of urea and soft segments of polyether glycol cross-linked by urethane. It possesses a combination of properties not available in other materials, outstanding of which are its sustained high modulus of elasticity, physiological compatibility, resistance to flex-fatigue and excellent stability over long implant periods. Table 7 compares the physical similarities

TABLE 7

COMPARISON OF PROPERTIES OF A POLYETHER URETHANE vs
A POLYESTER URETHANE (18)

Property	Polyether Urethane	Polyester Urethane
Tensile strength (psi)	6,700	5,840
Ultimate elongation (%)	750	540
Hardness, Shore A	75	88
Specific gravity (g/cc)	1.1	1.2
Stress at 100% elongation (psi)	850	700

of a polyester and a polyether polyurethane. Lyman and associates (19) have produced a polyurethane which shows good thromboresistance and Nyilas (20) has developed a copolymer of polyurethane and dimethyl siloxane which is reported to be similarly blood compatible.

Cure in place foams (Stafoam PE102, American Latex Products Corp.) were at times used for leaflets of artificial hearts but were subject to flex-fatigue as were Teflon cusps. Bone glues of polyurethane foam have also been used for repairing fractures but as many failures as successes have been reported with them.

Silicone Rubber

No other elastomer has been as widely used for biomedical applications as silicone rubber. The Dow Corning Corporation has kept abreast of these uses and has compiled an extensive medical bibliography on Silastic® in their bulletins (21). Careful formulation and quality control on the part of Dow Corning has kept variability at a minimum and can be credited with much of the success experienced with the polymer. The material is physically stable and can be relied upon to cause little or no tissue reactions; for medical grades only.

Chemically, the silicone rubbers are composed of repeating linear chains of cross-linked dimethyl siloxane. The elastomer is available as heat vulcanizing stocks, sponges, solvent solutions, air-drying adhesives and room temperature vulcanizing (RTV) casting compounds. (Also *see* molding materials, Ch. IV.)

Heat-vulcanizing Silicone Rubber

Heat-vulcanizing silicone rubber offers the greatest degree of physical strength of all Silastic compounds. Artificial hearts, heart valves and blood oxygenator films have been made from Dow Corning's Silastic 370, a low durometer rubber, Silastic 372, of medium durometer, and Silastic 373, of hard durometer. All three, complete with the catalyst dichlorobenzoyl peroxide, are supplied in the raw state by the manufacturer as MDX4-4514, MDX4-4515 and MDX4-4516 respectively. Table 8 gives their physical properties.

Although this material is inert in the majority of circum-

TABLE 8

TYPICAL PROPERTIES OF HEAT VULCANIZING MEDICAL
SILICONE RUBBER, SILASTIC (22)

Property	Soft Grade MDX 4-4514	Med. Grade MDX 4-4515	Firm Grade MDX 4-4516
Color	Clear; translucent	Clear; translucent	Clear; translucent
Specific gravity (g/cc)	1.12	1.14	1.23
Durometer hardness, Shore A	25	50	75
Tensile strength (psi)	850	1200	1000
Elongation (%)	600	450	350
Die B tear strength (psi)	70	75	75
Brittle point (F)	−175	−100	−100
Stiffening temperature (F)	−166	—	—
Dielectric strength, (v/mil)	500	540	540

All physical and electrical properties measured on ⅛ inch thick samples molded 5 minutes at 240 F and oven cured 1 hour at 480 F.

stances, Starr and co-workers (23) have found a small percentage of Silastic poppets of artificial heart valves to be adversely affected by blood "lipids." Carmen and Kahn (24) have shown that *in vitro* lipid absorption is increased with degree of cure of medical grade silicone rubber; the lipid uptake was also shown to decrease with silica filler content. They found the lipid to consist of fatty acids, neutral fat, steroid, steroid ester and phospholipid and was present from 0.1 to 5.5 wt% when associated with a 4 percent increase by volume. Eight hours of oven cure at 250 F, after molding, was found to reduce the lipid up-take (0.82 wt%). These findings have not been documented *in vivo*.

Silicone elastomer copolymers containing trifluoropropyl-methyl polysiloxane possess greater thromboresistance than conventional "medical grade" dimethyl polysiloxane and as a group are more oil resistant. Musolf and co-workers (25) have implanted these materials as vena cava rings and as right atrial probes. Verification of its overall capabilities remains to be established. (*See* special materials, Ch. I.)

Silicone Films

Silicone rubber films, silicone-coated Dacron and copolymerized "silicone-polycarbonate" and other combinations have been used as membranes for blood oxygenators. In Galletti's (26) review of plastics for membrane oxygenators, he describes the techniques, of Dantowitz and associates (27), for a microporous membrane. In particular, Dantowitz has developed a silicone-

TABLE 9

GAS TRANSMISSION RATES OF PLASTIC FILMS (21)

Film *	O_2 †	CO_2 †
Polyvinylidene chloride (Saran)	1.03	.78
Monochlorotrifluoroethylene (Trithene A)	1.5	16.0
Polyester (Mylar)	11.06	19.4
Cellulose acetate	110.0	560.0
Opaque high-density polyethylene	142.0	348.0
Polypropylene	187.0	639.0
Clear high-density polyethylene	226.0	1,030.0
Polystyrene	310.0	1,535.0
Low-density polyethylene	573.0	1,742.0
Tetrafluoroethylene (Teflon TFE)	1,100.0	3,000.0
Silicone rubber (Silastic 372 medical grade)	98,000.0	519,000.0

* measured at or calculated to .001 inch in thickness.
† Transmission rates expressed as cubic centimeters of gas transmitted through 1 mil film per 24 hours per 100 square inches of film, with one atmosphere pressure differential across the film; measured at 77 F. (cc/24 hrs/100 in²/atmosphere).

coated mesh of stainless steel which relies on a blend of graphite and Teflon emulsion to achieve high flow rates of oxygen and carbon dioxide when in contact with the blood. This design is reported by Galletti as being "the closest approximation to the natural lung yet devised." Not all materials are applicable for this use; Table 9 lists the gas transmission rates of various plastic films.

Silicone Rubber Sponge

Silicone rubber sponge has proved to be a valuable material for reconstructive surgery and maxillofacial prostheses. The sponge is composed of open or closed cells and can be readily cut to the desired shape for the filling of voids or defects where a soft, lightweight packing is desirable. Unfortunately, it is no longer commercially available. (*See* foaming, Ch. IV.)

Silicone, RTV, Casting Elastomer

Silicone RTV compounds are liquids or pastes that cure with the addition of a catalyst to durable, resilient elastomers. A number of products are available with various viscosities and curing agents for specific applications, such as electrical potting and encapsulating, sealing and caulking, and as a flexible mold material. (*See* encapsulation, Ch. III, and mold materials, Ch. IV.) Silastic 382, a RTV made especially for use with medical devices, has been found to be "well tolerated in the body and

TABLE 10

TYPICAL PROPERTIES OF SILASTIC 382 RTV MEDICAL
GRADE ELASTOMER (29)

Property *	Value
Specific gravity (g/cc)	1.13
Durometer hardness, Shore A	43
Tensile strength (psi)	400
Elongation (%)	160
Brittle point (F)	−100
Shrink, linear (%):	
after 3 days at 77 F	0.4
after 6 days at 77 F	0.6
after 14 days at 77 F	0.7
Water absorption (%) after 7 days	
immersion at 77 F	0.4
Thermal conductivity (cal/cm C sec)	0.525×10^{-3}
Volume coefficient of thermal expansion/C	
(0 to 100)	7.50×10^{-4}

After vulcanizing for 24 hours at 77 F with 0.5 pbw stannous octoate.
Note: Care must be exercised to select only medically approved materials as some commercially available RTVs are particularly toxic.

causes no irritation to tissues" (28). It is essential to use only
approved materials.

Table 10 lists typical properties of an RTV Medical Grade
Elastomer which is completely autoclavable.

PLASTICS

Plastics have two practical classifications: *thermosetting* and
thermoplastic. The thermosetting materials resemble concrete
in that once they have hardened into the desired shape, they
are irreversible. As a group they include the epoxies, castable
polyesters and the phenolics, of these only the epoxies have
found use in biomedicine. Conversely, the thermoplastic materials resemble wax in that they are capable of being melted and
shaped repeatedly. For example, they include the polyolefins,
cellophane, cellulose acetate, the fluorinated hydrocarbons,
Hydron®, polymethyl methacrylate, polycarbonate, polyvinyl
chloride, nylon and so forth.

Cellophane

Cellophane is made by the cuprammonium process and is
available as plain or moistureproof (that is, coated with a moisture repelling polymer, usually proprietary). The uncoated cel-

lulose, as manufactured for sausage casing (Visking, American Viscose Co. and Cuprophan® PT 150, J.P. Bemberg Co.), has been universally used for kidney dialysis membranes. The plastic is stiff but becomes soft and limp when immersed in water and acts as a selective filter for body fluids; Babb and co-workers (30) have determined its solute diffusivity. (*See* Table 11.)

Cellulose Acetate

Mason, Lindan and Sparks (31) have developed a cellulose acetate hemodialysis membrane cast from

Cellulose Acetate *	20 pbw
Formamide	30 pbw
Acetone	50 pbw

The film is reported to have higher dialysis coefficients for sodium chloride, sucrose, urea and vitamin B_{12} than does Cuprophane. Table 11 compares the properties of cellulose acetate with Cuprophane.

TABLE 11

COMPARATIVE PROPERTIES OF CUPROPHANE AND
CELLULOSE ACETATE DIALYSIS MEMBRANES (31)

	Cellulose Acetate		Cuprophane *	
Property	CA-1	CA-2	Axially	Longitudinally
Tensile strength (psi)	800 —	1200	1200–1600	4000
Ultimate elongation (%)	7.5		60–90	20–30
Membrane thickness (mil)	1.2 —	0.85		0.95
Water permeability (g/hr/cm²/atm)	2100	240		80

* Cuprophan® PT 150, J.P. Bemberg Co.
Note: Strength and stiffness in most films is greatest in the longitudinal direction due to molecular orientation brought on by stretching during the manufacturing process.

Epoxy Resins

These polymers are condensation products of epichlorohydrin with biphenols. In the uncured state, the resins range from low viscosity liquids to high temperature melting solids. Reaction with various curing agents promotes the cross-linkage necessary to transpose the resin into a stable, thermosetting plastic. Various curing agents can be used; such as the aliphatic and aromatic

---

* Eastman Chemical Co.

amines, anhydrides and polyamides. Table 12 gives typical curing agents for general purpose epoxy resins. Fillers can be added
to liquid epoxy to reduce cost, shrinkage, thermal coefficient of
expansion, peak exotherm, alter viscosity, electrical properties,
physical strength, and improve adhesion and abrasion resistance.
The fillers most commonly used are calcium carbonate, clay,
silica, barium sulfate, mica and various metallic oxides.

Borgstedt (33) describes the epoxy resins, their diluents,
curing agents and accelerators, as generally toxic. However, by
using special preparations the epoxies have proved valuable for
encapsulation of electronic implants (*see* encapsulation, Ch. III)
and as adhesives.

Salyer and co-workers (34) developed epoxy and urethane
resin systems which show good thromboresistance. (*See* special
materials, Ch. I.) Pluronic F-68®, a nonionic detergent, and
heparin were alternately used in various formulations to achieve
blood compatibility while having the versatility of being either
rigid, semirigid or flexible. These materials were demonstrated

TABLE 12

TYPICAL EPOXY CURING AGENTS (32)

Curing Agent	Parts/100 resin	Cure Schedule
I. *Aliphatic Polyamines*		
Diethylene triamine	10.9	R.T. or 1–2 hr @ 212 F
Triethylene tetramine	12.9	R.T. or 1–2 hr @ 212 F
Tetraethylene pentamine	14.3	R.T. or 1–2 hr @ 212 F
Amino ethyl piperazine	22.7	R.T. or 1–2 hr @ 212 F
II. *Aromatic Amines*		
Methylene dianiline	26.2	131 F + 2 hrs @ 252 F + 2 hrs @ 340 F
Metaphenylene diamine	14.3	131 F + 2 hrs @ 252 F + 2 hrs @ 340 F
III. *Anhydrides*		
Hexahydrophthalic anhydride	60–75	2 hrs @ 212 F + 2–6 hrs @ 302 F
Dodecenyl succinic anhydride	96–130	2 hrs @ 212 F + 4–6 hrs at 302 F
Tetrahydrophthalic anhydride	60–75	24 hrs at 248 F or 8 hrs at 302 F
IV. *Polyamides*		
Viscous	60–100	R.T. + 1–2 hrs at 212 F
Low viscosity	30–70	R.T. + 1–2 hrs at 212 F
V. *Aliphatic Cyclic*		
Ether amine	50	17 hrs @ 122 F

Note: Not intended for implants.

TABLE 13
RIGID ANTITHROMBOGENIC EPOXY SYSTEM (34)

Material	pbw
Epon 820 *	100
Diethylenetriamine	8–12
Pluronic F-68 †	3–5
Cure: 4 days @ 77 F	
Potlife, 20–30 minutes	

* Shell epoxy resin, diglycidyl ether of bisphenol A, Shell Chemical Co.
† A nonionic detergent, a polyol of a block copolymer of ethylene oxide and propylene oxide, Wyandotte Chemical Co.

as being useful for the fabrication of circulatory assist device components. Tables 13, 14 and 15 give the formulations for three types.

Gourley and Arnold (35) prepared a composite mixture of plaster of Paris and epoxy resin to produce a bone replacement suitable for segmental limb defects. Although the addition of the epoxy resin increased the strength of the composite, they concluded that it also rendered it incompatible with the tissues; based on control implants using the straight epoxy.

To produce their material they mixed commercial grade plaster of Paris with one-half by volume of water; separately they mixed equal volumes of an epoxy * and its hardener. The

TABLE 14
FLEXIBLE ANTITHROMBOGENIC URETHANE SYSTEM (34)

Material	pbw
CP-260 *	40
Carbowax 600 †	60
Heparin ‡	3
Toluene diisocyanate mix, Mondur	
TD-80§	55
Triethyl amine	~1.3
Cure: 17 hours @ 140 F	

* Voranol, Dow Chemical Co., tris(hydroxy-propyl)-glycerine.
† Union Carbide Corp., polyethylene glycol.
‡ Aqueous heparin is uniformly added to the CP-260 and Carbowax 600 and dried under vacuum until all water is removed.
§ An 80/20 mix of 2,4 and 2,6 toluene diisocyanate isomers, Mobay Chemical Company.

---

* Resiweld Plastic Alloy No. 620.

TABLE 15

SEMIRIGID ANTITHROMBOGENIC EPOXY SYSTEM (34)

Material	pbw
Epon 820	50
D.E.R. 732 *	50
Heparin †	3–8
Diethylene triamine (or	
Ajicure B-001‡, 50 pbw)	6.8–8.8
Cure: 17 hours @ 122 F	

* Dow Chemical resin, diglycidal ether of propylene glycol.
† Aqueous heparin is uniformly added to the
Epon 820 and D.E.R. 732 and dried under vacuum until all water is removed. The heparin
complex is then heated to 122 to 140 F for 60
minutes to promote chemical bonding.
‡ Aliphatic cyclic ether amine, Ajinomoto Co.

prepared epoxy resin was added to the prepared plaster of Paris
in alternate proportions of 1:4, 1:2, 3:4 parts by volume. These
were thoroughly mixed; cast into shape and allowed to set for
twenty-four hours. Implant studies have shown it to lose up to
50 percent of its strength *in vivo* (36) which makes it unsuitable
for many orthopedic applications.

Hill and Mouhot (37) developed a method of preparing
porous prostheses for artificial limbs using an epoxy resin system
diluted with a volatile solvent. Stockinette material is saturated
with the mix and the solvent is allowed to evaporate at room
temperature opening the interstices of the cloth. The appliance
is then cured for two hours at 203 F. Hill's system is based on
the following formulation:

Resin System	Parts by wt/70 g Stockinette
Epon 815 *	100
Versamid 140 †	50
Methylene chloride	100

Fluorocarbons

The fluorocarbons consist of straight chain polymers with
fluorine functional groups such as Teflon and those modified
with a chlorine group such as Kel-F®.

* Epoxy resin, Shell Chemical Company.
† Polyamide resin, General Mills Inc.

Teflon

Teflon *, polytetrafluoroethylene, is an opaque, flexible and relatively soft organic compound with thermal expansion properties nearly ten times that of metals. Teflon has a carbon-to-carbon chain with two atoms of fluorine attached to each carbon in a polymeric sequence. The polymer tends to cold flow under pressure and does not have the wear resistance of nylon or high density polyethylene. It has the lowest coefficient of friction, however, of all the plastics. This property gives the surface a slippery feeling to the touch and a self-lubricating quality.

Teflon cannot be molded using the conventional methods for thermoplastics. Instead, it must be raised to the gel state, 620 F, at which temperature it can be sintered or coined into the desired shape using methods comparable to those used in powder metallurgy. As a result, articles to be molded should be kept simple.

Teflon has an unusual degree of resistance to chemical attack and is uneffected by all solvents except for molten alkali metals and solutions of alkali metals.

Teflon initially attracted the attention of biomedical researchers because of its inherent environmental stability. Implantation tests showed it to be one of the least reactive polymers, *in vivo*. However, it could not withstand the rigors of cyclic-loading when used by orthopedic surgeons as a component of the total hip prosthesis.

Teflon has been widely used as fabric arterial prostheses.

TABLE 16

TYPICAL PROPERTIES OF TEFLON, PTFE (38)

Property	Solids	Films
Tensile strength (psi)	4500–4800	3000–4000
Ultimate elongation (%)	320–350	300–500
Specific gravity (g/cc)	2.15–2.20	2.15–2.20
Resistance to heat, Cont. (F)	500	500
Compressive strength (psi)	1700	1700
Hardness, Shore D	50–65	50–65
Modulus of elasticity ($\times 10^5$ psi)	0.58	0.58

Chemically inert to practically all chemicals and temperatures to 610 F.

* E.I. du Pont de Nemours Co., Inc.

However, when used as cusps for artificial heart valves the woven Teflon fatigued within a few months. Typical properties of Teflon, TFE, are given in Table 16.

Chlorotrifluorethylene, Kel-F *

Chlorotrifluorethylene polymer is produced from carbon, chlorine and fluorine. This thermoplastic is readily molded or machined using standard methods. It is translucent or transparent depending upon the degree of crystallinity present within the polymer. Translucent materials can be made transparent by heating sections to their molten state and then immediately

TABLE 17

TYPICAL PROPERTIES OF KEL-F (40)

Property	Value
Impact strength, Izod. (ft-lbs/in)	3.1–7.3
Tensile strength (psi)	4600–5700
Ultimate elongation (%)	125–175
Specific gravity (g/cc)	2.1
Resistance to heat, Cont. (F)	390
Dielectric strength, short time (v/mil)	530
Compressive strength (psi)	4600–7400
Hardness, Rockwell	M75–R95
Modulus of elasticity ($\times 10^5$ psi)	1.5–3.0

quenching the polymer in cold water; an amorphous condition results. Transparent Kel-F filters for heart-lung machines have been made in this fashion (39).

This polymer is slippery to the touch but does not have the wear resistance of nylon. It is extremely resistant to all chemicals except molten alkali metals and some aromatic and halogenated hydrocarbons cause it to swell slightly. Typical properties are given in Table 17.

Hydroxyethylmethylacrylate

Polyhydroxyethylmethacrylate, Hydron †, is a rigid acrylic polymer which has the ability to convert to an elastic gel by absorbing water. The chemical structure is similar to the polymethyl methacrylates but consists of a structural variation that

---

* Kel-F, Minnesota Mining and Manufacturing Company.
† Trademark of National Patent Development Corporation.

significantly alters its properties. Like the acrylics, Hydron has undistorted optical clarity. This water-white resin offers considerable promise for use as contact lenses, especially for those people who have difficulty adapting to conventional rigid acrylic contact lenses.

Hydron has great appeal for use in semirigid prostheses because of its physiological inertness and its ability to soften in aqueous environments without the use of plasticizers (41). This material can absorb between 3 to 90 percent of its weight of water depending upon the method used for polymerization.

The hydrophilic properties of Hydron have been used to advantage as a permanent soft liner for dentures under the trade name of Softdent *. Standard acrylic techniques are used (*see* casting, Ch. IV) to produce the denture, leaving a liner space of about 2 mm thickness in the area which will be adjacent to the gums. Once the denture is fully cured, the spacer is packed with Hydron. Reheating of the mold fully polymerizes the Hydron producing a hard denture base suitable for mechanical finishing; on soaking in water the liner becomes soft.

Users of this soft denture liner claim improved retention of their prosthesis due to increased capillary action between the wet surface of the liner and the naturally moist surface of the denture bearing tissues.

Levowitz and co-workers (42) have used the absorptive properties of Hydron to accept and elute a variety of therapeutic agents. The polymer was "charged" by the following mechanisms:

"1. Absorption by the dried Hydron.

2. Admixing with the polymer at time of polymerization.

3. In solution with Hydron S." (42)

The results of this work suggest further use of Hydron as a vehicle for administering therapeutic drugs.

Other applications include urinary catheters, prostheses for replacement of esophaegeal segments, and suture coating. Hydron is inert to strong agents such as hydrofluoric acid, which attack Teflon and Kel-F, and can only be depolymerized by heating above 392 F.

---

* Dentomed Company.

Ioplex 101®

Bixler and co-workers (43) have developed a polyelectrolyte complex called Ioplex 101 * which has been shown to be somewhat antithrombogenic. (*See* special materials, Ch. I.) This polymer is a complex of vinyl benzyltrimethylammonium chloride and styrene sulfonate; anticlotting characteristics seem to be associated with its sulfonate ion density. This elastomer can be reinforced with cloth and cemented to other surfaces by using a silicone adhesive. Shapes which are most readily fabricated are flat sheets and tubes. The material is sensitive to autoclaving and dry atmospheres; it has low tensile strength (that is, approximately 380 psi) and is easily torn.

Nylon

Nylon is a polyamide which has been used as components of prosthetic implants in the form of sutures, fabric and solids. Nylon 6.6 is the most commonly used variety and is a polycondensation product of adipic acid and hexamethylene diamine; all nylon contains free monomer which is constantly being released under implant conditions. Implant tests have shown nylon to be reactive and especially irritating when placed intraperitoneally and is usually accompanied by significant loss of tensile strength after a one year period. In hot water or after

TABLE 18

TYPICAL PROPERTIES OF NYLON (44)

Property	Value
Tensile strength (psi)	9000–12,500 *
Ultimate elongation (%)	29–225 *
Specific gravity (g/cc)	1.12–1.14 *
Resistance to heat, Cont. (F)	300 *
Compressive strength (psi)	13,000 *
	1,500 †
Hardness, Rockwell	R120
Modulus of elasticity ($\times 10^5$ psi)	0.5 *
	1.75—conditioned to 50% RH or
	4.15—dry †

* Nylon Type 6
† Nylon Type 6/6
Note: Not intended for implants.

* Amicon Corporation.

repeated autoclaving, nylon is particularly hygroscopic with deterioration of physical properties and dimensional loss. Table 18 gives typical properties of nylon.

Parylene C®

Parylene C *, poly (monochloro-p-xylylene), is a highly crystalline material. The polymer is made by pyrolyzing p-xylene at 1742 F in the presence of steam to produce a dimer. To apply the polymer as a coating to a surface, the dimer is heated in a sublimation chamber and pyrolyzed in the vapor phase at about 1022 F to form the monomer. When the monomer cools to 122 F

TABLE 19

TYPICAL PROPERTIES OF PARYLENE-C (45)

Property	Value
Tensile strength (psi)	13,000
Elongation to break (%)	200
Density (g/cc)	1.289
Melting temperature (F)	536–572
Glass transition temperature (F)	176–212

or below, immediate polymerization occurs. Table 19 gives the physical properties of Parylene C.

Parylene is a convenient coating for electronic components where a film of insulation is required over sharp edges and recesses. (*See* encapsulation, Ch. III.)

Polycarbonate

Polycarbonate resins are transparent linear polymers made from bisphenol A. They are tough, rigid and possess high impact resistance that yields rather than shatters. Typical properties are given in Table 20. They are uneffected by oils or acids. Room temperature exposure to water has little effect, however continuous boiling in water will cause hydrolysis with concommitant loss of properties. Like the polymethyl methacrylates they are soluble in chlorinated hydrocarbons, aromatic esters and ketones. Unpigmented polycarbonate has met the National Sanitation Foundation's standard for use with potable water and has the Food and Drug Administration's sanction for use in process-

* Union Carbide Corp.

TABLE 20

TYPICAL PROPERTIES OF POLYCARBONATE (46)

Property	Value
Tensile strength (psi)	9000 to 10,500
Ultimate elongation (%)	110
Impact strength, Izod. (ft-lbs/in)	12 to 1.6
Specific gravity (g/cc)	1.2
Heat distortion temperature (F @ 66 psi)	285
Compressive strength (psi)	10,300 to 10,800
Hardness, Rockwell	M73 to 78
	R115 to 125
Modulus of elasticity ($\times 10^5$ psi)	3.0 to 3.5

ing and packaging of food. Polycarbonate lends itself well to standard molding methods and has been used by Boretos and co-workers (47) to thermoform transparent calvariums for monkey skulls. (*See* thermoforming, Ch. IV.) These implants have remained intact for periods up to one year without noticeable adverse effects, either locally to the brain or generally. Polycarbonate has been also used in the manufacture of oxygenators for heart-lung bypass operations.

Polyethylene

Polyethylene is a polyolefin polymer having a milky-white, translucent and wax-like surface. Three densities are available with tensile strength, hardness and chemical resistance increasing as the density increases. Although this class of materials is resistant to all acids, alkalis and inorganic chemicals and has no known solvent at room temperature, it will dissolve readily in a number of common solvents at 140 F. Table 21 gives typical

TABLE 21

TYPICAL PROPERTIES OF LOW, MEDIUM AND
HIGH DENSITY POLYETHYLENE

Property	Value Low Density	Medium Density	High Density
Molecular weight	3–4000	100–200,000	500,000
Specific gravity (g/cc)	0.912–0.925	0.926–0.940	0.941–0.965
Tensile strength (psi)	1100–1600	1700–1800	3400–37000
Ultimate elongation (%)	150	125–150	400–500
Impact strength, Izod (ft-lb/in)	no break	—	0.7–20
Resistance to heat, Cont. (F)	180	230	250
Dielectric strength, short time, (v/mil)	460–700	460–650	450–500
Hardness, Shore	D41–D46	D50–D60	D60–D70
Compressive strength (psi)	—	—	2700–3600
Modulus of elasticity ($\times 10^5$ psi)	0.14–0.38	0.25–0.55	0.6–1.8

TABLE 22

POSSIBLE ALTERATIONS TO POLYETHYLENE

I. Molecular Alterations
    a. Use of other monomers
    b. Cross-linking
        1. Using a cross-linking agent
        2. Using electron-beam irradiation
II. Additives
    Hexene or butene
    Antioxidants
    Ultraviolet stabilizers
    Fillers
    Antistatic agents
    Air or gas
    Others

properties of polyethylene in low, medium and high densities. The greater the molecular weight, the more resistant polyethylene is to hydrolytic degradation. Some polyethylenes fall into the ultrahigh molecular weight range—that is, 1½ to 2 million.[*] These have been used by orthopedic surgeons for polyethylene acetabular cups of the total hip prostheses.

Stability of high density materials can also be attributed to the presence of few side chains, a closely packed crystalline structure and only a few molecules of different size. Increased molecular weight is associated with an increase in strength, toughness and chemical resistance.

Polyethylene, like vinyl and other plastics and rubbers, is subject to alteration by use of additives. These changes, along with possible difference in molecular weight could account for discrepencies in performance as reported in the literature. Table 22 lists typical additives used with polyethylene.

Polyethylene (Polyethylene CL-100, Phillips Petroleum Company) can be conveniently rotation molded to produce parts able to withstand severe impact when tested at temperatures from −20 to 73 F. (*See* rotational molding, Ch. IV.) The resin is supplied as a powder combined with a peroxide cross-linking agent. The length of the curing cycle will depend on the degree of cross-linking desired for specific properties. Another polyethylene (Epolene C, Tennessee Eastman) of low density has been used as meltable cores or molds for fabricating artificial heart

[*] Hyfax 1900, Hercules Powder Company, and RCH-100, a German polyethylene product.

chambers of silicone rubber or segmented polyurethane. (*See* molding, Ch. IV.)

Expanded polyethylene sheets (Plastazote, Expanded Rubber and Plastics Ltd.) have been cut to shape with a sharp knife and used for cervical, spinal, metatarsal, heel, arm, elbow and hand splints for patients suffering from various maladies.

Polymethyl Methacrylate

The acrylics are thermoplastics of crystal clear appearance. They are light in weight, tough, durable, flexible in thin section, transmit light around corners, have low water vapor diffusion constants, resistant to the effects of light, oxygen and hydrolysis. The polymer has a high degree of ultraviolet transmission but can be made to absorb ultraviolet by special compounding. It will not support fungus growth and is immune to attack by these organisms; it is resistant to most mineral acids, alkalies and hydrocarbons. (*See* Table 23 for properties.)

Subcutaneous implants have shown little foreign body reaction, however, intraperitoneal shavings evoke a prolific foreign body reaction. Clinical use of molded implants (skull and tissue implants) have demonstrated it to be well tolerated even though other studies have shown that traces can be found in urine many weeks after implantation; the lungs are very sensitive to monomer vapor.

Casagrande and Danahy (49) caution against the use of unpolymerized methylmethacrylate in contact with the sciatic nerve when securing a prosthetic acetabular component of the artificial hip. They attribute fibrosis and contraction of the nerve to the heat that is liberated during curing.

TABLE 23

TYPICAL PROPERTIES OF POLYMETHYL METHACRYLATE (48)

Property	Value
Specific gravity (g/cc)	1.18
Refractive index	1.49
Tensile strength (psi)	8,000–10,000
Compressive strength (psi)	14,000–18,000
Ultimate elongation (%)	2.5–5.4
Resistance to heat, Cont. (F)	140–200
Dielectric strength, short time (volts)	500
Hardness, Rockwell	M80–M105
Modulus of elasticity ($\times 10^5$ psi)	3.5–4.5

Kelly (50) has studied the flexure-fatigue of polymethyl methacrylate and has shown that heat-cured resin is more resistant to flexure-fatigue than cold-cured resin; an important factor in construction of a denture or any prosthetic device subject to stress-relaxation deformation.

Although the acrylics are most often used as single component injection molding granules or powders, the dentist, neurosurgeon and orthopedic surgeon use a two component system. The pure methyl methacrylate monomer liquid is added to a powdered pre-polymer; the monomer plasticizes the polymer to a dough-like consistency for molding. (*See* injection molding, Ch. IV.) A more insoluble resin can be had by cross-linking with 1% to 2% of glycol dimethyl acrylate.

Mathewson (51) has developed an obturator made from radiopaque methyl methacrylate. An impression of the patient's defect is made by packing alginate elastic impression material into the pharyngeal area. The firm alginate is removed and the acrylic cast into it. A mixture of three parts of a self-curing acrylic powder is mixed with one part micronized barium sulfate and shaken well inside a plastic bag. The liquid portion of the self-curing acrylic resin is added to the powder and the mixture packed into the alginate impression. The entire assembly is autoclaved at 30 psi for ten minutes; the finished plastic piece is removed from the alginate, cleaned and polished.

A number of homologs of this polymer exist with varying properties. (*See* Table 24.)

TABLE 24

SOFTENING TEMPERATURES OF VARIOUS POLYMETHACRYLATE ESTERS (52)

Homolog (poly-)	Softening Temp. (F)
Methyl methacrylate	257
Ethyl methacrylate	149
N-Propyl methacrylate	101
Isopropyl methacrylate	203
N-Butyl methacrylate	92
Isobutyl methacrylate	158
Sec-Butyl methacrylate	144
Tert-Amyl methacrylate	169
Phenyl methacrylate	248

Polypropylene

Polypropylene offers a balance of properties not available with other polymers. It is semitranslucent and milky-white unless artificially pigmented and is easily processed by standard molding methods. Outstanding properties are low specific gravity, good rigidity, strength and hardness, resistance to chemical attack by most acids, bases and solvents, and enduring flex-fatigue resistance. The latter feature has given birth to numerous integral hinge designs. Table 25 gives typical properties. Medical

TABLE 25

TYPICAL PROPERTIES OF POLYPROPYLENE (53)

Property	Value
Tensile strength (psi)	5000
Stiffness in flexure (psi)	160,000
Heat distortion temperature (F at 66 psi)	220
Specific gravity (g/cc)	0.904
Hardness, Rockwell R	90–100
Flexural strength at yield (psi)	6000
Impact strength, Izod (ft-lb in)	0.3
Compressive strength (psi)	5500–8000
Hardness, Rockwell	R80–110
Modulus of elasticity ($\times 10^5$ psi)	1.6–2.25

applications are extremely varied and appear in sundry uses such as syringes, catheters, anesthesia and hospital supplies and equipment. For implant use, polypropylene components make up parts of blood oxygenators and kidney dialyzers. Detmer and co-workers (54) have found it to be of advantage in low-profile prosthetic heart valves.

Polyvinyl Alcohol

Polyvinyl alcohol can be given a wide range of properties depending upon the degree of polymerization and percent hydrolysis which is present. As many as eight grades * are commercially available. Where minimum water sensitivity is desired, the hydrolyzed grades are preferred; where a soft and flexible object is desired, the partially hydrolyzed grades are best. Viscosity is used as a measure of molecular weight, there-

* Elvanol, E.I. du Pont de Nemours Co., Inc.; Elvanol 72–60.

fore, the high and medium viscosity grades possess greater strength.

Odian and Leonard (55) have attempted to develop a cross-linked polyvinyl alcohol film for membrane hemodialysis that would maintain an open diffusional matrix and have adequate mechanical strength, insolubility and appropriate large molecule impermeability. They used a polyvinyl alcohol resin with a molecular weight of 250,000 * and modified it with allyl methacrylate. These films appear to be useable in clinical dialyzers in the same manner as cellophane.

Polyvinyl Alcohol Sponge †

Polyvinyl alcohol sponge is formaldehyde cross-linked, polyvinyl alcohol blown into a cellular structure using CO_2. When dry, this material is hard but can be readily softened by soaking in water; the wet material can be cut into simple shapes with scissors or scalpel.

Varying results with this material have been reported. For instance, when used as a patch graft or valve repair, the material changed properties, calcified and weakened.

Cobey (56) has found it to work successfully for traumatic and osteoarthritic joints in many patients. The sponge was interposed between the joint surfaces and held in place by growth of the synovium from the margins of the joints. The desired thickness of PVA was achieved by pressing the sponge between two aluminum plates and autoclaving it to induce a permanent set of from $\frac{1}{16}$ to $\frac{1}{8}$ inch thick.

Atlas and Venne (57) have used Ivalon® sponge for the repair of sliding hiatal hernias and have found it well tolerated and stable in this application after two years; contrary to other experience.

Probably no other material, except for silicone rubber, has been as widely used for clinical medicine as Ivalon sponge. The reason for most of this early use has been attributed, by Lee and Neville (58), to its availability in a sterile form, good early

---

* Elvanol, E.I. du Pont de Nemours Co., Inc., Elvanol 72–60.
† Unipoint Ind.; no longer available as Ivalon from Clay-Adams Co.

results and familiarity on the part of the surgeon. Successful use of this material, *in vivo,* seems dependant upon the application, as does many other polymers.

Polyvinylidene Chloride

Polyvinylidene chloride, Saran® (Dow Chemical Co.), exhibits high solvent and chemical resistance, low water absorption and moisture permeability. It is odorless, tasteless, tough, abrasion resistant and has good electrical characteristics. Plasticizers are required to produce soft and flexible properties. (*See* Table 26.)

TABLE 26

TYPICAL PROPERTIES OF POLYVINYLIDENE CHLORIDE (59)

Property	*Value*
Specific gravity (g/cc)	1.65–1.72
Tensile strength (psi)	3000–5000
Ultimate elongation (%)	less than 250
Impact strength, Izod. (ft-lbs/in)	0.3–1.0
Resistance to heat, Cont. (F)	160–200
Dielectric strength, short term (v/mil)	400–600
Compressive strength (psi)	2000–2700
Hardness, Rockwell	M50–M65
Modulus of elasticity ($\times 10^5$ psi)	0.5–0.8

Note: Not intended for implants.

Murphy and co-workers (60) have developed electrets which have shown some success in reducing clot formation. Films of polyvinyl chloride-vinylidene chloride, Saran I-8, were treated by heating the polymer to its softening point, applying a D.C. bias of 5 to 50 kv/cm, and allowing the specimen to cool to room temperature before short-circuiting the system. (*See* special materials, Ch. I.)

Polyvinyl Chloride

Polyvinyl chloride is basically a hard and horny material which derives flexibility, exhibited in some grades, to the addition of plasticizers. The amount of plasticizer used depends upon the extent of flexibility that is desired. Pliable polyvinyl chloride is used in the manufacture of extracorporeal blood tubing and blood bags, maxillofacial prostheses, medical and dental tubing, chambers and equipment for blood oxygenator pumps, and the administration of anethesia. A typical medical formulation for

TABLE 27

TYPICAL PROPERTIES OF A FLEXIBLE POLYVINYL CHLORIDE
FOR MEDICAL USE (62)

Property	Value
Tensile strength (psi)	2000–2100
Ultimate elongation (%)	400
Durometer hardness, Shore A	66–72
Dielectric strength (v/mil) (rapid rise method)	394
Temperature range:	
Dry heat (F)	215
Low temperature flexibility (F)	0
Brittle temperature (F)	−40
Autoclaving limits	1 hr @ 15 psi
(*See* sterilizing, Ch. VII.)	

flexible vinyl would consist of a high molecular weight polyvinyl chloride resin, a plasticizer such as dioctyl phthalate in concentrations up to 50 percent and a small amount of a calcium-zinc inorganic complex to serve as a stabilizer. Some manufacturers may use an epoxide-soybean plasticizer-stabilizer combination (61). Such a formulation would have properties similar to those shown in Table 27.

Food handling equipment consists of components made from polyvinyl chloride to process milk, ice cream, bake goods, beverages and packaging. Interest has been shown over the possible cumulative effects that leaching of plasticizers or stabilizers may have upon the body through various means of contact.

Meyler and co-workers (63) have shown that polyvinyl chloride tubing containing organic tin compounds interferes with cardiac contraction of the perfused rat's heart, whereas barium-cadmium stabilizers had no effect. An ester of phthalic acid, judged to be di-2-ethylhexyl phthalate by Meyler, used in both polyvinyl chloride formulations, was of low toxicity.

More recently, Jaeger and Rubin (64) have reported the presence of leached plasticizer stored in the body. They conjectured on the possible relationship of these materials to the well known but little understood phenomena of shock-lung syndrome.

SPECIAL MATERIALS WITH ANTITHROMBOGENIC SURFACES

Very important to the successful performance of a vascular prosthesis is its ability to inhibit the formation of blood emboli or thrombus build-up. A great part of biomedical research during the past decade has been dedicated to finding surfaces which would be essentially nonthrombogenic. In a recent article (65), Gott has summarized the work in this area and has catagorized thromboresistant surfaces according to three catagories: heparinized materials, surfaces with anionic radicals or imposed negative charges, and surfaces of relative inert material. Many of these have been previously discussed. Table 28 gives conclusions based on polymer rings placed in the "vena cava" of dogs and implant experience.

The GBH coating, graphite-benzalkonium-heparin, mentioned as surface 1 in Table 28 was developed by Gott (66) and is used to bind heparin to surfaces such as polycarbonate and polymethyl methacrylate; Teflon film, polyethylene and silicone rubber cannot be coated because of adhesion difficulties. The stepwise procedure consists of first applying a fine coating of graphite (Dag 154, 0.5μ to 2μ particle size, Acheson Colloids Co.) to the plastic. The graphite solution as supplied by the manufacturer is diluted with two parts of 95% ethyl alcohol and one part benzene. The clean plastic is immersed into the solution for five minutes and quickly redipped and oven dried at 122 F for forty-eight hours.

For polymethyl methacrylate, the Dag 154® is reduced with three parts of alcohol, omitting the benzene. Flexible plastics are treated with a solution of three parts of xylene to one part Dag 35® and air dried between each of two coats. The dried graphite coating is then baked at 250 F for one hour.

Following the above graphite surface coating, the prosthesis is immersed in 1:1000 aqueous benzalkonium chloride for five minutes and rinsed in saline. This is followed by a ten-minute immersion in heparined saline (that is, three parts saline to one part heparin). Gas sterilization must be used since autoclaving will destroy the activity of the heparin.

A TDMAC-heparin treatment referred to as surface 2 from Table 28 was developed by Grode and associates (67) and is applicable to silicone rubber. The procedure consists of solvent swelling the polymer to increase permeability and then soaking it in a solution of tridodecyl methyl ammonium chloride

TABLE 28

CLASSIFICATION OF THROMBORESISTANT SURFACES (65)

    I. Heparinized surfaces
       1. GBH (66)
       2. TDMAC—heparin (67)
       3. Epoxy—heparin (34) Table 13 and 15
   II. Surfaces with anionic radicals or imposed negative charges
       1. Anionic polyelectrolyte (43)
       2. Acrylate with anionic surfactant (2)
       3. Carboxylated cellulose
       4. Negatively charged electrets (60)
  III. Surfaces of relatively inert materials
       1. Pyrolytic carbon
       2. Albuminated polystyrene
       3. Fluorinated silicone rubber (25)
       4. Acrylic hydrogel, Hydron (42)
       5. Epoxy with Pluronic (34), Table 13
       6. Polyurethane copolymer, S.R.I. (19)
       7. Segmented polyether urethane (18)
       8. Polyurethane-silicone copolymer (20)
       9. Polyurethane-polyvinyl-graphite
     10. Stellite with tallow polish for heart valves.
     Others that could be included:
     11. Teflon, highly polished
     12. Silastic
     13. Titanium for heart valves

(TDMAC). The treated polymer is then immersed in a heparin solution to bond the anticoagulant to the surface.

Other materials developed for blood compatibility and not listed in Table 28 have been previously discussed. (*See* epichlorohydrin, natural rubber and polyurethanes, Ch. I.)

FABRICS AND THREAD

Fabrics have been used in vascular grafts, septal defects, outflow tract patches, sutures, reinforcement for rubber implants and many others. The most widely used materials are Dacron, nylon and Teflon, Orlon®, silk, polypropylene, and Teflon-coated Dacron. Halpern (68) reported the durability of five fabrics after two-year periods of implantation. (*See* Table 29.) Postlethwait (69) conducted a similar study with sutures and found that cotton and silk lost tensile strength and silk was absorbed; nylon showed a "moderate decrease in tensile strength but caused the least tissue reaction; polypropylene maintained its tensile strength and showed low tissue reaction until the late intervals when slight fragmentation of a few sutures occurred;

TABLE 29

STABILITY OF PLASTIC FABRIC AND SUTURE IMPLANTS

Material	Approximate Implant Period (yrs)	Change in Tensile Strength
Cotton	2	severe (68)
Dacron	2	slight (68, 69)
Nylon	3	moderate (69)
Orlon	2	severe (68)
Polypropylene	2	slight * (69)
Silk	2	absorbed (69)
Teflon	2	slight (69)

* Associated with some fragmentation.

and Dacron maintained tensile strength and caused a moderate tissue reaction."

Although some fabrics are thermoplastic and moldable, only applications involving "heat-setting" or "pleating" of vascular grafts have been reported.

REFERENCES

1. Taken in part from *Technical Data Book SIA*. General Electric Company, Waterford, New York.
2. Leonard, F., Nelson, J., and Brandes, G.: Vulcanizable saturated acrylate elastomers. *Ind Eng Chem*, 7:1053, 1958, and Leonard F., Nielson, D.A., Fadali, A.M., and Gott, V.L.: *J Biomed Mater Res*, 3:455, 1969.
3. Byck, J.S., Chow, S., Gonsior, L.J., Miller, W.A., Mulvaney, W.P., Robeson, L.M., and Spivak, M.A.: Polymeric materials for circulatory assist devices. *Artificial Heart Program Conference*. N.H.I., U.S.D.H.E.W., 123–132, 1969.
4. Personal communication, C.J. Jankowski.
5. Wright, J.S., Johnston, J.B., and Luber, L.J.: Thrombus resistance of intravascular implants of chlorosulphonated polyethylene. *J Thorac Cardiovasc Surg*, 5:740, 1966.
6. Report BL–329: *Hypalon 20 for Food Conveyor Belt Covers*. E.I. du Pont de Nemours and Co., Inc., Wilmington, Delaware.
7. *Cure Systems for Hydrin 200 Elastomers*. B.F. Goodrich Co., Cleveland, Ohio.
8. Grode, G.A., Falb, R.D., Takahashi, M.T., and Leininger, R.J.: Nonthrombogenic Hydrin rubber. Unpublished data.
9. Horsley, J.: *Surgery of the Blood Vessels*. St. Louis, C.V. Mosley Co., 1915, p. 70.
10. Atsumi K., Sakurai, Y., Atsumi, E., Narausawa, S., Kunisawa, S.,

Okikura, M., and Kimoto, S.: Application of specially cross-linked natural rubber for artificial internal organs. *Trans Am Soc Artif Intern Organs*, 9:324–331, 1963.

11. Nose', Y., Wright, J., Mathis, M., and Kolff, W.J.: Natural rubber artificial heart. *Digest 7th Intern Conf on Med and Bio Engr*, 1967, pp. 379.

12. Weber, D., Kon, T., Williams, C., MacDermott, H., Peabody, D., Mrava, G., and Nose', Y.: *Proc 22nd Ann Conf Engr Med Biol*, 1969, pp. 24–10.

13. Imai, Y., von Bally, K.; Nose', Y.: New elastic materials for the artificial heart. *J Am Soc Artif Intern Organs*, 16:17–25, 1970.

14. Cook, G.B.: A thermoplastic balloon for endometrial diagnosis. *Missouri Med*, 60:1132–1134, 1963.

15. Jones, R.H., and Wei, Y.K.: Application of trans-1,4 polyisoprene in orthopedic and rehabilitation medicine. *J Biomed Mater Res*, 1:19–30, 1971.

16. Mirkovitch, V., Akutsu, T., and Kolff, W.J.: Polyurethane aortas in dogs. Three-year results. *Trans Am Soc Artif Intern Organs*, 8:79–83, 1962.

17. Sharp, W.V., Gardner, D.L., and Andresen, G.J.: A bioelectric polyurethane elastomer for intravascular replacement. *Trans Am Soc Artif Intern Organs*, 12:179–182, 1966.

18. Boretos, J.W., and Pierce, W.S.: Segmented polyurethane: A polyether polymer. *J Biomed Mat Res*, 2:121–130, 1968.

19. Lyman, D.J., Brash, J.L., and Klein, K.G.: The effect of chemical structure and surface properties on synthetic polymers on the coagulation of blood. In *Proceeding Artificial Heart Program*, edited by R.J. Hegyeli. USGPO, Washington, D.C., 1969, p. 113.

20. Nyilas, E.: Development of blood-compatible elastomers: Theory, practice and *in vivo* performance. *23rd Conference on Engineering in Medicine and Biology*, 12:147, 1970.

21. *Bulletin of the Dow Corning Center for Aid to Medical Research*. Dow Corning Corp., Midland, Michigan.

22. *Clean-Room, Dow Corning Silicone Rubber Compounds*. Dow Corning Corp., Midland, Michigan, Feb. 1970.

23. Starr, A., Pierie, W.R., Raible, D.A., Edwards, M.L., Siposs, P.E., and Hancock, W.D.: Cardiac valve replacement, Experience with the durability of silicone rubber. *Circulation (suppl.)*, 33 and 34:I-116–I-123, 1965.

24. Carmen, R., and Kahn, P.: *In vitro* testing of silicone rubber heart-valve poppets for lipid absorption. *J Biomed Mater Res*, 2:457–464, 1968.

25. Musolf, M.C., Hulce, V.D., Bennett, D.R., and Ramos, M.: Development of blood compatible silicone elastomers. *Trans Am Soc Artif Intern Organs*, 15:18–23, 1969.

26. Galletti, P.M.: Applications of plastics in membrane oxygenators. *J Biomed Mater Res, 1*:129–134, 1971.
27. Dantowitz, P., Borsanyi, A.S., Deibert, M.D., Snider, M.T., Scherler, M., Lipsky, M.H. and Galletti, P.M.: A blood oxygenator with preformed membrane-lined, capillary channels. *Trans Am Soc Artif Organs, 15*:138–143, 1969.
28. Braley, S.: The chemistry and properties of the medical-grade silicones. *J Macromol Sci Chem, A4*:529–544, 1970.
29. Dow Corning Medical Materials Data, Dow Corning Corp., Midland, Michigan, May 1963.
30. Babb, A.L., Maurer, C.J., Fry, D.L., Popovich, R.P., and Ramos, C.P.: Methods for the *in vivo* determination of membrane permeabilities and solute diffusivities. *Trans Am Soc Artif Intern Organs, 14*:25–30, 1968.
31. Mason, N.S., Lindan, O., and Sparks, R.E.: Reinforced celluose acetate dialysis membranes. *Trans Am Soc Artif Intern Organs, 14*:31–35, 1968.
32. Taken in part from Naturman, L.I.: *Plastics Technology, 16*:31, 1970.
33. Borgstedt, H.H.: Toxic hazards of epoxy resins. *Indust Med Surg, 32*:426–429, Oct. 1963.
34. Salyer, I.O., Blardinelli, A.J., Ball, G.L., III, Weesner, W.E., Gott, V.L., Ramos, M.D., and Furuse, A.: New blood compatible polymers for artificial heart applications. *J Biomed Mater Res, 1*:105–127, 1971.
35. Gourley, I.M.G., and Arnold, J.P.: The experimental replacement of segmented defects in bone with a plaster of Paris-epoxy resin mixture. *Am J Vet Res, 21*:1119–1122, Nov. 1960.
36. Welsh, R.P., and Macnab, I.: Ceramics in surgery. *J Biomed Mater Res Symposium, 2*:231–249, 1972.
37. Hill, J.T., and Mouhot, H.G.: Porous epoxy laminates. *J Cellular Plastics, 4*:155–158, 1968.
38. Taken in part from (a) *Information Bulletin, Teflon TFE-fluorocarbon resin dispersions, properties, and processing techniques.* E.I. du Pont de Nemours and Co., Inc., Wilmington, Delaware, and (b) *Plastics Technology Processing Handbook.* Plastics Technology. 1969–1970, pp. 265.
39. Fluorocarbon aids heart surgery. *Modern Plastics, 38*:104–105, Nov. 1960.
40. *Kel-F brand Halofluorocarbon polymers.* Minnesota Mining and Manufacturing Co., Jersey City, New Jersey.
41. Simpson, B.J.: Hydron: A hydrophilic polymer. *Biomed Eng, 4*:65, Feb. 1969.
42. Levowitz, B.S., LaGuerre, J.N., Calem, W.S., Gould, F.E., Scherrer, J., and Schoenfeld, H.: Biologic compatibility and applications of Hydron. *Trans Am Soc Artif Intern Organs, 14*:82–88, 1968.

43. Bixler, H.J., Cross, R.A., and Marshall, D.W.: Polyelectrolyte complexes as antithrombogenic materials. In *Artificial Heart Program Conference*, edited by R.J. Hegyeli. Supt of Docs, USGPO, 1969, pp. 79–86.
44. *Plastics Technology Processing Handbook*. Plastics Technology. 1969–1970, pp. 268.
45. *Bakelite Parylene General Information*. Process Data, Union Carbide Corp., New York, New York.
46. *Design Tips, Lexan Polycarbonate Resin*. General Electric Company, Pittsfield, Mass.
47. Boretos, J.W., Bourke, R.S., Nelson, K.M., Naumann, R.A., and Ommaya, A.K.: Technique for unilateral isolation of the subdural space in the intact primate. *J Neurosurg*. 35:101–107, 1971.
48. *Plastics Technology Processing Handbook*. Plastics Technology, 1969–1970, pp. 263.
49. Casagrande, R.A., and Danahy, P.R.: Delayed sciatic-nerve entrapment following the use of self-curing acrylic. *J Bone Joint Surg* [*Am*], 53-A:167–168, 1971.
50. Kelly, E.K.: Flexure fatigue resistance of heat-curing and cold-curing polymethyl methacrylate. *JADA*, 74:1273–1276, 1967.
51. Mathewson, R.J.: The use of a micronized barium in an obturatior construction. *Cleft Palate J*, 7:862–866, 1970.
52. Power, P.O.: *Synthetic Resins and Rubbers*. New York, John Wiley & Sons, Inc., 1943, pp. 150.
53. *A Guide to Hercules Polyolefins*. Hercules Powder Company, Wilmington, Delaware.
54. Detmer, D.E., McIntosh, C.L., Boretos, J.W., and Braunwald, N.S.: Polypropylene poppets for low-profile prosthetic heart valves. *Ann Thorac Surg*, 13:122–127, 1972.
55. Odian, M., and Leonard, E.F.: Synthesis and evaluation of graded polyvinyl alcohol membranes. *Trans Am Soc Artif Intern Organs*, 14:19–24, 1968.
56. Cobey, M.D.: Arthroplasties using compressed Ivalon sponge. *Clin Orthop*, 54:139–144, 1967.
57. Atlas, H., and Venne, J.P.: La prothese d'Ivalon dans la cure chirurgicale de la hernie hiatale par glissemenk. *L'Union Med du Canada*, 99:1879–1881, 1970.
58. Lee, H., and Neville, K.: *Handbook of Biomedical Plastics*. Pasadena, Pasadena Technology Press, 1971, pp. 15, 21.
59. Modern Plastics Encyclopedia. *Modern Plastics*, 48:568, Oct. 1971.
60. Murphy, P., Holly F., Van Someren, L., Bankole, M., Singh, S., and Bernhard, W.F.: Antithrombogenic properties of electrified polymers. *Trans Am Soc Artif Intern Organs*, 13:131–137, 1967.
61. Hollenbaugh, W., U.S. Stoneware Co.: Personal communication.
62. Bulletin T-97, *Tygon Flexible Plastic Tubing*. The U.S. Stoneware Company, Akron, Ohio.

63. Meyler, F.L., Willebrands, A.F., and Durrer, D.: The influence of polyvinyl chloride (PVC) tubing on the isolated perfused rat's heart. *Circ Res, 8:*44, 1960.
64. Jaeger, R.J., and Rubin, R.J.: Plasticizers from plastic devices: Extraction, metabolism, and accumulation by biological systems. *Science, 170:*460–462, 1970.
65. Gott, V.L., and Akira, F.: Antithrombogenic surfaces, classification and *in vivo* evaluation. *Fed Proc, 30:*1679–1685, 1971.
66. Gott, V.L., Whiffin, J.D., Koepki, D.E., Daggett, R.L., Boake, W.C., and Young, W.O.: Techniques of applying a graphite-benzalkonium-heparin coating to various plastics and metals. *Trans Am Soc Artif Intern Organs, 10:*213–217, 1964.
67. Grode, G.A., Anderson, J.J., Grotta, H.M., and Falb, R.D.: Nonthrombogenic materials via a simple coating process. *Trans Am Soc Artif Intern Organs, 15:*1, 1969.
68. Halpern, B.D.: Polymers in medicine and surgery—a survey. *Ann NY Acad Sci, 146:*193–202, 1968.
69. Postlethwait, R.W.: Long-term comparative study of nonabsorbable sutures. *Ann Surg, 171:*892–898, 1970.

II

————————————————————————————Compounding

THE PROPERTIES of base materials can be varied by incorporating two or more ingredients in definite proportions by weight. To modify specific polymer properties, compounding offers a convenient means of altering viscosity, cure rate, gas permeability, tear strength, electrical properties and adhesion to metals and fabrics. Further, it provides a means of improving resistance to degradation by weather, ozone, heat, oxygen, compression-set, flex-cracking, abrasion, low temperature embrittlement, water and aqueous substances, oils, chemicals and solvents.

Frequently, tailoring for the optimum in any one characteristic may lead to a sacrifice in some other property; all requirements of processing and ultimate use must, therefore, be constantly kept in mind and evaluated. Numerous additives are commonly used to achieve these purposes. Specific classes with examples (in parentheses) follow:

Accelerators (mercaptans, thiazoles, guanidines): Can reduce the time and temperature required to achieve a given state of cure to an elastomer.

Antioxidants (aromatic amines or substituted phenols): Inhibit degradation of physical properties of some polymers because of oxidation; though oxidation is catalyzed by heat and sunlight, it can occur in a cool, dark environment.

Antiozonants (waxes, quinoline derivates): Incorporation of small percentages in polymers provide ozone resistance.

39

Peptizers (guidelines, thiurams): Assist in compounding by having a softening effect on elastomers.

Plasticizers (petroleum oils, special organic liquids, vegetable oils, resins and other polymers): Improve compound processing characteristics and modify vulcanizate properties, such as hardness, elasticity and stability at low temperatures.

Release Agents, Lubricants and Extrusion Aids (stearic acid, petrolatum, paraffin): Improve ease of extrusion, aid in wetting and dispersion of fillers, facilitate mold flow and mold release.

Retarders (salicylic acid, phthalic anhydrides): Inhibit premature vulcanization; it is preferable, however, to eliminate accelerators rather than add retarders.

As used in polyvinyl chloride, polyvinyl alcohol, polyurethanes and most synthetic rubber, the aforementioned are not recommended for chronic use when implanted *in vivo*, since they have been known to migrate out of polymers and may generate toxic reactions.

Reinforcing Agents and Fillers (carbon blacks, clays, whitings, silicas, metallic oxides): May be nonreinforcing, semireinforcing or reinforcing on basis of their effect on tensile strength and elastic modulus of a polymer. Their effects are different for each situation; for example, reinforcing agents for thermosetting resins may be nonreinforcing when used in elastomers or thermoplastics, and vice versa.

Reinforcing agents and fillers often react with raw rubber to produce a condition known as "crepe hardening." The longer the raw materials are stored after addition of such ingredients, the more pronounced is this effect. The shelf-life of the raw rubber, or "crepe," is largely limited by the development of this condition and may render the crepe too "nervy" to mold or if molded the product will warp or shrink. The rate at which "crepe hardening" occurs depends upon the type and amount of filler being used, the specific polymer or base, and the addition of softener, if applicable.

Vulcanizing or Cross-linking Agents (sulfur, peroxides, amines, metallic oxides): Cross-linking, required in most elastomers and thermosetting materials (*see* epoxy, Ch. I) to realize optimum properties, is not required for most thermoplastics.

Many variations of cross-linking agents are possible for any one material.

For rubber, vulcanization is an important and necessary procedure to develop good elastic properties. Furthermore, the transformed polymer is nonplastic, solvent insoluable,* higher in tensile properties and more resistant to abrasion and temperature degradation. Sulfur, peroxides, amines and metallic oxides can be used as vulcanizing agents for rubber. To bring out special properties requires a careful balance of ingredients and proportions.

Sulfur in excess quantities can hasten vulcanization, whereas smaller than normal amounts of sulfur if used in combination with an accelerator can shorten the time and temperature necessary for optimum curing. This is particularly true for natural rubber.

Silicone rubber stock (other than RTVs) used for medical implants is vulcanized using 2, 4-dichlorobenzoyl peroxide in a 50% active paste. Various molding times and oven curing temperatures as well as the amount of vulcanizing agent can effect durometer hardness, tensile strength and elongation limits (1).

Backrinding or torn areas present at the parting line of a molded silicone rubber piece is dependent primarily on the mold temperature (*see* pressure molding, Ch. IV) relative to the decomposition rate of the peroxide. For instance, molding of silicone balls for ten minutes at 220 F produces greater integrity of the parting line than molding at either 240 or 250 F. The presence of "rotten-spots" is caused by a reaction between oxygen from entrapped air and the free radicals of the peroxide vulcanizing agent (2). If the problem cannot be corrected by proper mold design, then a less sensitive peroxide should be used; unfortunately the choice for nontoxic materials is not many.

* *Note:* Generally, vulcanized rubber does not completely dissolve, rather, it may swell to as much as 300 percent when immersed in solvents such as benzene, hexane, chloroform and carbon tetrachloride. This feature can be used to great advantage when fabricating a tightly fitting rubber sleeve over a form of fixed dimension. Rubber tubing can be dilated by the appropriate solvent and slipped in place. Air or oven drying will shrink the rubber against the form, as it tries to regain its original dimensions.

Figure 1. Conventional 13-inch, 7½ hp rubber mill. Rollers, internally bored to allow for steam or chilled water circulation, revolve at 1:1.3 ratio.

MILLING

In this method of compounding, an open roll mill (Fig. 1) softens polymers preparatory to incorporating other ingredients. Each rubber or plastic responds differently to milling. Be certain to clean all polymers or chemicals from the rolls before each use. The two rolls of a typical mill may operate at ratios of either 1.2 to 1, 1.3 to 1, or 1.4 to 1 to achieve necessary shearing and mixing of high viscosity stocks. Adjustment of the clearance between rolls helps control mixing. The faster moving roll should operate at a peripheral speed of about 75 to 90 feet per minute for the 12-inch diameter size. A nylon scraper blade positioned to act, at will, against the fast roll helps sheet off the rubber at intervals during mixing. An exhaust directly over the mill along with a pan under the rolls help keep stray materials under control.

Figure 2. Compounded rubber being sheeted from the mill and ready for molding.

For materials such as silicone rubber, the standard rubber mill need only be equipped with cooling water circulating through its rollers. The purpose of the cooled rollers in this instance, is to prevent premature vulcanization or a preliminary loss of vulcanizing agent due to heat build-up beyond 130 F (1). The investment in equipment and space does not always allow for more than one such unit in a small developmental laboratory. To extend the rubber compounding capabilities to such materials as acrylate, polyurethane, butyl and natural rubbers, provision can be made to heat the rolls, usually by steam.

To insure through mixing of ingredients on the mill, the following suggestions are of value:

1. To achieve a smooth rolling bank of polymer, set the rolls tightly together; open the gap as the rubber becomes soft.
2. Add only a small amount of each ingredient at a time but as quickly as uniform mixing will allow.
3. Materials other than silicone rubber require warming the rolls to 130 F to soften the polymer.
4. If additives are incorporated into the polymer, observe this sequence:
   a. Antioxidants and antiozonants
   b. Retarders or accelerators
   c. Peptizers
   d. Fillers
   e. Plasticizers
   f. Vulcanizing agents and accelerators
5. Continually cross-blend the rubber until uniform throughout.
6. Keep the rubber's heat history to a minimum.
7. A masterbatch of part of the polymer and all of the additives is often a desirable means of mixing.
8. Remove from mill, cool and mold.

Figure 2 shows the compounded rubber being sheeted from the mill and ready for molding.

Although a Banbury mixer, a machine with a set of intermeshing teeth, can also be used to incorporate additives to rubber, a good roller mill mix can possess 200 to 400 psi higher tensile properties.

REFERENCES

1. *Compounding with Silastic gums and bases, Silicone-fluorosilicone.* Dow Corning Corp., Midland, Michigan.
2. Alliger, G., and Sjothun, I.J.: *Vulcanization of Elastomers.* New York, Reinhold Publishing Company, 1964.

III

Encapsulation of Implants

FOR THE ELECTRONIC ENGINEER interested in monitoring or controlling physiological parameters, through telemetry or by direct connection to a subject, precautions must be taken to protect the device from the body's corrosive environment while precluding adverse effects on the animal or patient. Coating or encapsulation of implants conveniently provides for reducing the deleterious effects of moisture, streamlining contours to facilitate cleaning and sterilizing, imparting ruggedness and rigidity, preventing signal frequency shifts caused by movement or vibration, and minimizing tissue abrasion, inflammation and related physiological response.

Adverse reactions can be generated by physical or mechanical shortcomings. Shape, size and weight depend crucially upon the particular site selected for the implant. Tissues, nerves and blood vessels are easily damaged by undue force or pressure exerted by an instrument, sharp corners, protrusions or abrasive surfaces. Erosion through the skin has been observed as a result of improperly secured implants (1). Care must be exercised, when closing the tissues over the implant, to avoid dead space which can permit migration of the device. Frank and co-workers (2) have used a sack of Teflon mesh over pacemaker units to fix their position within the body.

Chardack and associates (3) implanted the first transistorized pacemaker in 1960, using an epoxy encapsulated unit. Shortly thereafter, Levitsky and co-workers (4) used silicone rubber to protect an implanted telemetry device designed for long-term stimulation of the heart. A device for electrostimula-

45

TABLE 30

ELECTRONIC IMPLANT MOISTURE-PROOFING VARIATIONS *

Varnish
Acrylic with PVC coating
Acrylic with epoxy coating
Epoxy
Natural rubber with silicone grease †
Silicone rubber with wax
Half paraffin and half beeswax
Glass with epoxy coating
Welded can

* Not necessarily inert without a covering of medical grade silicone rubber or equal.
† Stability not known.

tion of the bladder to facilitate evacuation in paraplegic dogs was similarly insulated by Kantrowitz and Schamaum (5). A number of electronic implants for diverse functions followed, with various schemes to add inertness and extend the useful life of the device (6–11). Table 30 lists those materials most often used for moisture proofing electronic implants.

Although encapsulation techniques are simple in principle, difficulties are encountered in obtaining void-free castings with negligible shrinkage, low heats of reaction and complete polymerization. To achieve high-density castings, the unit should be degassed under vacuum immediately after pouring to eliminate entrained air. Breakage of fine wires and shifting of operating characteristics occasionally result from epoxy encapsulation. Mackay (12) states that the embedding process can "shift the frequency of a high frequency transmitter by 20 percent; that is, a 100 MHz oscillator can drop in frequency by 20 MHz . . . or enough to take the transmitter out of the range of its intended receiver." To protect delicate assemblies from stress, some investigators apply a preliminary coating of a RTV silicone or natural rubber (no heat or shrinkage involved) over the circuitry prior to casting with resin. Shrinkage and exothermic heat during curing of epoxies can be reduced by incorporating an inorganic filler, such as calcium carbonate, into the resin. Factory-insulated electronic parts often contain waxes and phenolics which act as cure inhibitors, preventing ultimate properties from developing. Absorptive utensils should not be used when mixing resins which require critical amounts of curing agent; polyethylene cups and stainless steel spatulas are good choices.

The ability of a protective coating to resist the influence of water is of paramount importance. Circuitry, moist from water trapped within the unit or permeating through its insulation, promotes corrosion, shorting and changes in impedance, particularly if salts are present in the water.

Organic materials, often thought to be waterproof, do transmit water to varying degrees. There is no direct relationship between the amount that permeates, that which is absorbed, and the deterioration of the polymer during immersion. Some plastics and rubbers may absorb small quantities of water but permit considerable flux. Materials with extremely low moisture vapor transmission rates, as shown in Table 31, eventually reach a state of equilibrium. Others, such as polymethyl methacrylate, silicone rubber and the various epoxies, have relatively high permeability to moisture but are easily cast or used as a coating. Of these three, the epoxies, especially those cross-linked with an aromatic amine (20) or an anhydride, offer the best moisture resistance. Nevertheless, Mackay (12) has observed the resistance of a one-megohm, epoxy-coated, glass-enclosed thermistor to drop 0.8 MΩ after one week in isotonic saline. Critchfield and associates (21) have found that packages encapsulated with

TABLE 31

MOISTURE VAPOR TRANSMISSION OF SEVERAL POLYMERS

Polymer (2-mil films)	Moisture Vapor Transmission (Measured at 86 F and 90%–98% R.H.) g/mil/100 in²-24 hr
Polymonochlorotrifluoroethylene:	
Aclar 33-C (13, 14)	0.015
Kel-F (15)	0.02
Trithene (16)	0.02
Ethylene/vinyl acetate copolymer (Elvax 260), 1-mil film (17)	0.20
Polyvinylidene chloride (Saran) (18, 19)	1
Parylene C (18)	1
Polytetrafluoroethylene (Teflon) (18, 19)	3
Polyethylene (18)	21
Polyethylene terephthalate (Mylar) (18)	48
Polystyrene (18)	120
Silicone rubber, 1-mil film (19)	170

TABLE 32

IN VIVO EXPERIENCE WITH VARIOUS INSULATED
ELECTRONIC IMPLANTS

Device	*Insulation*	*Months of Useful Service*
Cortical electrodes (25)	Epoxy coating	Acute
Flow transducer (26)	Cast acrylic with PVC cement coating	12
Motility transmitter (23)	Latex coating with silicone lubrication	1
Pacemakers (1, 3, 27, 28)	Cast epoxy with Silastic coating	1 to 14
R. F. receiver (4)	Silastic coating	2
Strain gauge (29)	Varnish with Silastic coating	3
Temperature transmitter (10)	Glass with epoxy and Silastic coating	2
Transmitter (30)	Acrylic or styrene with cast epoxy and Silastic coating	4

epoxy-Silastic and epoxy-glass-Silastic layers require four times the mass and five to ten times the volume of the circuitry to afford effective protection from body fluid leakage.

Mackay (12) suggests that the most reliable protection from moisture is afforded by a coating consisting of a mixture of half paraffin and half beeswax. Goodman and Gibson (22) have improved on the brittleness, cracking and high expansion coefficient of refined paraffin by including 20 percent by weight ethylene/vinyl acetate copolymer (Elvax 260®). "Electrical leakage characteristics measured over an immersion period (in physiological saline) of more than 37,000 hours (over 4 years) show values in excess of 10^{13} ohms across about a 0.125 mm dipped thickness." Lonsdale and co-workers (23) have improved natural latex insulation by rubbing silicone grease into the outer surface, and Enger and Rhinelander (24) have reduced the water and electrolyte permeability of Silastic by the addition of spermaceti wax. *In vivo* performance in all of these, however, remains to be firmly established. Other investigators have tried several combinations of insulation in a variety of contexts with varying degrees of success. A number of these are listed in Table 32. In most cases, silicone rubber has been used as a top coat to minimize tissue reactions.

Thompson (31) has solved the problem of waterproofing implantable cardiac pacemakers by placing components in a stainless steel can filled to within $1/16$-inch of the top with silicone rubber and closed with a heliarc welded lid. To prevent general overheating during welding, the can is placed in a bed of wet sand. Batteries should not be sealed intimately with other electronic components, since battery gassing generates harmful moisture.

Electronic devices will continue to play a role as surgical implants. As instrumentation develops, long-term reliability and miniaturization will become an integral part of systems designed to function for major organs and neurological networks; the development of polymers with more stable properties will play a major role in this advancement. Electronic engineers of today are planning for the future (32).

REFERENCES

1. Reininger, E.J., and Hinchey, E.J.: Variable-frequency cardiac pacemaker for use with the trained unanesthetized dog. *J Appl Physiol,* 24:580, 1968.
2. Frank, H.A., Zoll, P.M., and Linenthal, A.J.: Long-term electrical stimulation of the heart: Present status. *J Thorac Cardiovasc Surg,* 57:17, 1969.
3. Chardack, W.M., Gage, A.A., and Greatbach, W.: A transistorized, self-contained, implantable pacemaker for the long-term correction of complete heart block. *Surgery,* 48:643, 1960.
4. Levitsky, S., Glenn, W.W.L., Mauro, A., Eisenberg, L., and Smith, P.W.: Long-term stimulation of the heart with radiofrequency transmission. *Surgery,* 52:64, 1962.
5. Kantrowitz, A., and Schamaum, M.: Bladder evacuation in paraplegic dogs by direct electrical stimulation. *JAMA,* 187:127, 1964.
6. Bradley, W.E., Chou, S.N., and French, L.A.: Further experience with the radio transmitter receiver unit for the neurogenic bladder. *J Neurosurg,* 20:953, 1963.
7. Bassett, A.L., Pawluk, R.J., and Becker, R.O.: Effects of electric currents on bone *in vivo. Nature* [*Lond*], 204:652, 1964.
8. deVilliers, R., Nosé, Y., Meier, W., and Kantrowitz, A.: Long-term continuous electrostimulation of a peripheral nerve. *Trans Am Soc Artif Intern Organs,* 10:357, 1964.
9. Hawthorne, E.W., and Harvey, E.: Telemetering of ventricular circumference in dogs. *J Appl Physiol,* 16:1124, 1961.
10. Balin, H., Busser, J. H., Hatke, F., Fromm, E., Wan, L.S., and Israel, S.L.: Radio telemetry system for the study of ovarian physiology. I. Instrumentation. *Obstet Gynec,* 24:198, 1964.
11. McCoy, E.J., and Bass, P.: Chronic electrical activity of gastroduodenal area: Effects of food and certain catecholamines. *Am J Physiol,* 205:439, 1963.
12. Mackay, R.S.: *Biomedical Telemetry, Sensing and Transmitting Bio-*

logical Information from Animal and Man. New York, John Wiley & Sons, 1968.

13. *Product Data Sheet A–1–660, Aclar Fluorohalocarbon Film.* General Chemical Division, Allied Chemical Corporation, New York.

14. News Release #P-355: *Thermistor Insulation Technique Developed by Sippican for Biomedical Applications.* The Sippican Corp., Marion, Mass., January 15, 1969.

15. *Kel-F Halofluorocarbon Polymers.* Minnesota Mining & Mfg. Co., Jersey City. N.J.

16. *Trithene Film.* Visking Company, Chicago, Illinois.

17. Dupont Technical Information Sheet, #PL4–1168, *Elvax 260 Vinyl Resin.* E.I. du Pont de Nemours & Co., Inc., Wilmington, Del.

18. *Union Carbide Process Data, Bakelite Parylene General Information.* Union Carbide Corp., New York.

19. *Gas Transmission Rates of Plastic Films Chart.* Dow Corning Center for Aid to Medical Research, Midland, Mich.

20. Lee, H., Cupples, A.L., Neville, K., Culp, G.W., and Schubert, R.J.: Development of improved encapsulation materials for implantation. In *Artificial Heart Program Conference,* edited by R.J. Hegyeli. Washington, D.C., Supt. of Documents, U.S.G.P.O.

21. Critchfield, F.H., Jr., Critchfield, F.H., Neuman, M.R., and Lin, K.Y.: Experimental study of packaging materials for microelectronic implants. *Proceeding of the 21st Annual Conference on Engineering in Medicine and Biology,* 1968, p. 9A4.

22. Goodman R.M., and Gibson, R.I.: BioInstrumentation. A sealing material for implanted devices. *Bioscience, 20:*1066, 1970.

23. Lonsdale, E.M., Steadman, J.W., and Pancoe, W.L.: A telemetering system for securing data on the motility of internal organs. *IEEE Trans Biomed Eng, 13:*153, 1966.

24. Enger, C.C., and Rhinelander, F.W.: Implantable impermeable flexible encapsulants for artificial organs. *J Biomed Mat Res, 1:*149–168, 1971.

25. Bartlett, J.R.: Insulating micro-electrodes by centrifuging. *Electroenceph Clin Neurophysiol, 21:*305, 1966.

26. Goodman, A.H.: A transistorized squarewave electromagnetic flowmeter. II. The flow transducer. *Med Biol Eng, 7:*133, 1969.

27. Towsend, J.F., Stoeckle, H., and Schuder, J.C.: Tissue and electrode changes in chronic cardiac pacing—An experimental study. *Trans Am Soc Artif Intern Organs, 11:*132, 1965.

28. Zoll, P. M., Frank, H.A., Zarsky, L.R.N., Linenthal, A.J., and Belgard, A.H.: Long-term electric stimulation of the heart for Stokes-Adams disease. *Ann Surg, 154:*330, 1961.

29. Ehle, A.L., and Foltz, E.L.: A miniature mercury strain gauge for chronic nonobstruction measurement of intestinal motility. *J Appl Physiol, 26:*223, 1969.

30. Ko, W.H., and Nueman, M.R.: Implant biotelemetry and microelectronics. *Science, 156*:351, 1967.
31. Thompson, N.P.: Personal communication.
32. Portions of this chapter are based on Boretos, J.W.: *IEEE Transactions, IECI-17*:151–155, 1970.

IV

───────────Molding Methods and Materials

MOLDING OFFERS definite advantages over machining (*see* machining, Ch. VI) and has been recognized as an important part of fabrication. Among those benefits most often considered are increased production rates and lower costs. For the biomedical materials laboratory, molding also offers increased design capabilities in such areas as the application of intricate or complex shapes and the use of special materials that cannot be machined; also it provides for the development of unique properties through compounding.

Many molding methods used for producing a medical device have been empirically derived to meet a specific need while others are either of a conventional nature or a modification of techniques common to industry. Those methods most often used are casting and embedding using acrylic resin, epoxy resin and silicone RTV rubber; coating by means of dip coating, dipping, mandrel coating and painting; electrodeposition of polymers; foaming of open and closed-cell sponges; compression, injection and transfer molding; extruding; rotational molding; blow molding; thermoforming and others.

Special materials must be used to meet particular molding requirements. For example, precision machined metal molds are necessary for high-pressure molding of extended durations; low melting alloys are ideal for low-pressure molding, meltable cores and short durations; electroplated molds provide shapes which are difficult to machine; duplicating materials such as agar-agar, alginate, gelatin, polysulfide rubber and acrylamide gel are helpful for obtaining impressions of body parts; and latex, vinyl and gypsum are simple to use materials for casting molds.

The first section of this chapter is devoted to molding methods as applied to biomedical engineering; the second section will discuss mold materials.

MOLDING METHODS

The biomedical-plastics fabrication facility must have basic molding capabilities. Each specialty will be treated separately.

Casting and Embedding

Gravity and vacuum casting are the two easiest means of handling liquid polymers—that is, the least amount of expensive tools and equipment is necessary. The method has been applied to insulating implanted electronic components (*see* encapsulation, Ch. III), embedding museum specimens, obtaining impressions or casting molds. Usually liquid polymer is mixed with its cross-linking agent and poured about an object. To eliminate entrained air, the assembly can be placed in a vacuum chamber and cycled one or more times at a negative pressure of 10 to 15 psi. Once the polymer has solidified and cured, the molded object is ready for use.

Centrifugal force has also been used in the casting and embedding process; it increases the density of the resin through exclusion of entrapped air. The process is similar to gravity and vacuum casting except that the encapsulated object is centrifuged just prior to solidifying. The acrylic resins, epoxy resins and silicone RTV rubbers have been used in this manner. Examples of each are given in the second section on molding materials.

Acrylic Casting

The acrylic, or polymethyl methacrylate, monomers are low viscosity, water-white, volatile liquids that can polymerize to a transparent solid under the influence of heat, light or organic peroxides. These features make them ideal for the preservation and display of specimens; Table 33 gives typical properties. If

TABLE 33

PROPERTIES OF METHYL METHACRYLATE LIQUID MONOMER * (1)

Property	Value
Specific gravity (g/cc)	0.9497
Refractive index (nD 15.6)	1.4168
Boiling point (F)	
at 760 mm Hg	212
at 200 mm Hg	142
at 100 mm Hg	115

* "Lucite," Plastics Dept., E.I. du Pont de Nemours Co., Inc.

the object can withstand heat and pressure, other molding methods should be used (*see* pressure molding, Ch. IV), however, if it is fragile, embedment can be accomplished by the following casting methods:

DIRECT SYRUP METHOD. The specimen is prepared by washing in alcohol and acetone followed by drying under vacuum for several hours. The acrylic casting syrup is prepared by partially polymerizing the liquid monomer in a water-bath with a reflux condenser at 194 to 212 F until a thick but pourable fluid results. If heating takes longer than four hours, a trace of inhibitor is most likely present and can be neutralized by adding 0.02 percent by weight benzoyl peroxide (Luperco AC, Lucidol Corp.). The syrup is carefully poured into the mold and subjected to moderate vacuum until all entrained bubbles are brought to the surface. The mold is then placed in an oven or water-bath at 105 F and cured for seven to ten days.

LAYER-ON-LAYER METHOD. This method is similar to the direct syrup method except provision is made for the reduction of heat formed bubbles and shrinkage. Thin layers are successively built-up by pouring separate ½ inch thicknesses un-

TABLE 34

TYPICAL PROPERTIES OF SOLID POLYMETHYL METHACRYLATE (1)

Property	Value
Specific gravity (g/cc)	1.18
Tensile strength (psi)	10,000
Impact strength, Izod.(ft.lb/in)	0.3
Hardness, Rockwell H	80
Heat distortion temperature (F)	
(ASTM D648-42T)	199
Light transmission, visible range (%)	92
Index of refraction	1.49

til the entire mold is filled. Increasing the temperature to 160 F will reduce the curing time, for each layer, to twenty-four hours. Typical properties of fully cured acrylic casting resin are given in Table 34.

Optimum performance with acrylic casting is achieved by observing the following:

1. Acrylic resin monomer contains an inhibitor which must be removed before casting. This is achieved by vigorously shaking the monomer several times with an equal volume of 2% sodium hydroxide solution in a separatory funnel; the layers are allowed to separate and are drawn off. Distilled water is then substituted for the sodium hydroxide solution and the washing procedure repeated. Small amounts of residual water can be eliminated by allowing the monomer to stand overnight, in a refrigerator, in contact with anhydrous sodium sulfate or calcium chloride. The latter are removed by simple filtering.

   A more complex method of removal of inhibitor is vacuum distillation at 212 F and 200 Hg.

2. Copper and copper molds inhibit polymerization.

3. Organic specimens containing water can interfere with polymerization.

4. Shrinkage can cause distortion; protect delicate objects with a preliminary coating.

5. The larger the mass of the casting, the greater is the risk of bubbling through overheating.

6. Post-curing at 195 to 212 F for several hours will insure complete polymerization.

Winkler and McCullen (2) have described a cold curing variation for casting acrylic. A catalyst (available from Vernon-Benshoff Co.) is used to preclude the need for heat in the curing process and the molding time is reportedly shortened.

Fairchild and Kelly (3) have devised a method for centrifugal casting of acrylic dentures. A gypsum mold is prepared, in the usual manner, with porcelain teeth in-place and having a cavity representing the gingival area. The cavity is provided with a polyethylene spout to the outside. A mixture of 30 cc of acrylic polymer granules and 10 cc of liquid monomer is poured into the spout and the mold is rotated at 650 rpm for thirty minutes. A conventional centrifugal casting machine is converted to accommodate the mold. Heat is then applied until the acrylic is fully cured. This method of molding complex items with inserts, such as dentures, is believed to be faster than the usual flasking and reflasking, packing and testing procedures necessary for pressure molding.

Epoxy Casting

The epoxy resins have been widely used for potting of electronic components; epoxies offer a degree of protection from the physiological environment for such implanted devices as cardiac pacemaker and telemetry devices (*see* encapsulation, Ch. III). Molds for molding artificial heart valves made from

Figure 3. Heart valve mold made from cast epoxy resin. Polyurethane is cast into the mold, the two halves clamped together and allowed to cure at room temperature. (Used by permission of the *Journal of Thoracic and Cardiovascular Surgery.*)

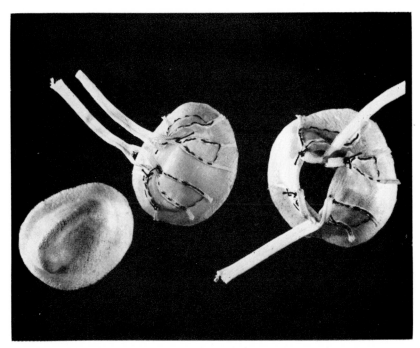

Figure 4. Cloth-reinforced heart valves of polyurethane. (Used by permission of the *Journal of Thoracic and Cardiovascular Surgery*.)

polyurethane foam have been constructed from a quick curing epoxy (Plastic Steel, Devcon B liquid type, Devcon Corp.) by Braunwald and co-workers (4). This material consists of 80% finely powdered steel and 20% epoxy resin. No heat or pressure are required and two hours after the addition of the hardener, the casting is converted into a permanent and durable mass. Figure 3 shows the mold and Figure 4 shows the polyurethane heart valves made in this mold.

Epoxy casting resins are cross-linked with either an amine, anhydride or amide (*see* epoxy, Ch. I). Shrinkage which can be as much as 4 percent is greatly reduced by the addition of reinforcing agents such as calcium carbonate, silica and others. An extensive list of commercial epoxy casting formulations is available (5).

The viscosity of epoxy resins can be reduced to make them flow more readily by including up to 20 percent of either phenyl

or allyl glycidyl ether. Only minor changes in the overall properties are affected since these mono-epoxy compounds combine
chemically with the cured resin (6).

Bartlett (7) has used centrifugal principles to insulate micro-
electrodes with an epoxy resin (Epoxylite 6001M, Epoxylite
Corp.) or a varnish (Insl-X; Insl-X Co. Inc.). His method is reported to eliminate the frustrating experiences associated with
achieving uniform coatings. A conventional electric fan is modified to operate at 500 rpm and a balanced arm is attached to the
motor shaft. The electrodes are attached opposite each other
and at right angles to the balance arm so that they face inward.
The electrodes are dipped into the insulation, removed and the
motor started. The bead formed at the tip is driven up the shaft
of the electrode by the centrifugal force; flow varies with viscosity and can be regulated by the rate of turning. The pieces
are revolved until dry and then removed and cured at 122 to
158 F for twenty-four hours.

Polyester resins are also of value for casting and although
they show higher shrinkage than the epoxies they are advantageous where water-white casting are required. One of these
(Castolite, The Castolite Co.) has been widely used for embedment of biological specimen and microtome sections.

Silicone RTV Casting

Frank and Yoder (8) have described a method of making
flexible casts of the lung with silicone RTV; the material is
forced into the tissue under hydrostatic pressure equivalent to
a 25 cm column of water. Prior to injecting the rubber, the lungs
may be dried, however, this is not necessary and may introduce
artifacts. Silastic RTV 382 (Dow Corning Corp.) was thinned,
in this instance, with 26 percent by weight medical silicone oil
to achieve the desired viscosity (*see* materials, Ch. IV); the
specimen was tilted and rotated to encourage even distribution
throughout the tiny channels. The rubber was allowed to cure
for two to three days before attempts were made to remove the
overlying tissues. Hydrochloric acid was used for that purpose;
silicone rubber is unaffected by the cold acid.

Segarra (9) has suggested a method of embedding histological specimens which can be retrieved, if desired, for further

study. The method involves the use of a water-clear RTV silicone potting compound (LTV-602, General Electric Co.) and is reported to be simpler, quicker and less expensive than embedding with polymethyl methacrylate. The specimen is first dehydrated with two 24-hour soaks in, first, 80% alcohol and then in absolute alcohol. These are followed by one soak in xylene for one to two days and another in the RTV for a similar period. Thus prepared, the actual casting can begin; fresh RTV is mixed with its catalyst (10 to 20 drops per 100 ml of RTV). The bottom of a suitable box is covered to a shallow depth with the mixed RTV and vacuum aereated. Once this preliminary, supporting layer has set, the specimen is put in place and a second mix is poured over it to complete the casting.

Coating

Coating consists of such processes as calendering, dip coating, dipping, mandrel coating, painting or spraying and hand lay-up methods.

Calendering

Calendering is designed to sheet out rubber and plastics to a predetermined thickness by passing the polymer between a series of tightly set rolls. Laboratory size units generally consist of three or more rolls and can be stacked or interchanged depending on the application. Figure 5 shows the arrangement. Unlike the rubber mill, the rolls revolve at a 1 to 1 ratio. Like the mill, temperature control is accomplished by use of circulating

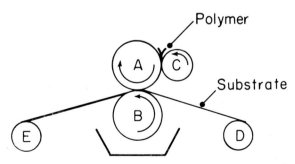

Figure 5. Typical arrangement of rollers for a laboratory calender. A = coating roller; B = drive roller; C = doctor roller; E = take-up roller.

water or steam (*see* compounding, Ch. II). Thin layers of rubber can be applied to cloth or other backing materials in this manner.

Dip Coating

This method involves the coating of webs or other substrates with rubber or plastic from solution. Usually the substrate is fed through a bath of solvated polymer where the appropriate amount is applied, then through a heated chamber to drive off

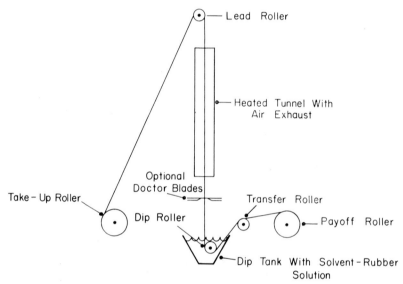

Figure 6. Typical arrangement for dip coating cloth with rubber.

residual solvent and cross-link the film. Figure 6 shows a typical arrangement for coating Dacron or nylon with silicone rubber. Doctor blades may or may not be used to control the build-up. (*See* appendix for definitions of terms.)

Dipping

Dipping is of value for making plastic and rubber objects such as balloons, membranes, nipples, surgical gloves and so forth. It utilizes simple forms or molds and is capable of producing thin films which would be difficult to mold in any other way.

Lee and co-workers (10) have made films for blood clotting tests from polyvinyl alcohol by dipping stainless steel mandrels into a hot 30% solution of Elvanol® (PVA, E.I. du Pont de Nemours Co., Inc.) in water and drying. Complete drying is accomplished by immersing the stabilized PVA in a stirred acetone bath followed by oven baking. To remove the cast films from their steel mandrels the entire unit is cooled to −152 F; the difference in contraction between the two materials allows them to separate. Polished Teflon was also used as a mandrel, however, Teflon specks broke away from the surface after several uses.

Figure 7. A rack and pinion device for dipping latex. A mandrel is clamped by means of a drill-chuck. A slow-speed reversing motor driven through a variable rheostat provides control.

Merendino (11) reports the use of dipping methods for producing prosthetic heart-valve leaflets from solutions of polyurethane (Estane, B.F. Goodrich Co.).

Natural rubber has been used for artificial hearts and paramedical needs. (*See* natural and acrylate rubber, Ch. I). The dipping procedure (12, 13) for all of these is similar and can be represented by the following:

1. *Unsupported films*
    a. A form can be made from stainless steel, porcelain, aluminum, glass, low-melting alloys and others. (*See* mold material, Ch. IV.)
    b. Dip the form into an alcoholic slurry of 25% by weight talcum or sodium bicarbonate and air dry.
    c. Then, into a coagulant made from the following:
        1000 cc methanol
        540 cc H_2O
        400 gm calcium nitrate
        60 cc glacial acetic acid
    d. Air dry thirty to sixty seconds while constantly rotating to evenly distribute the coagulant.
    e. Dip into latex at a steady, even speed. Surface smoothness and build-up is a function of the rate of insertion and amount of coagulation which occurs. Figure 7 shows an easy to assemble rack-and-pinion device for this purpose.
    f. Allow the form to remain in the latex until the desired thickness is achieved. (*See* Table 35 for deposition rate.)
    g. Remove form and rotate as before to evenly distribute any remaining droplets.
    h. Air dry until the latex is firm.
    i. Soak the rubber in lukewarm water that is constantly being changed with fresh water, according to the schedule in Table 36.
    j. Remove from water and dry according to Table 36.
    k. Cure in over for thirty minutes at 200 F.

Latex rubber (Lotol 6982N, Natural Rubber Dipping Compound for Surgical Goods, U.S. Rubber Co.) processed in this manner can withstand autoclaving at 15 psi for fifteen minutes

TABLE 35

TYPICAL DEPOSITION RATE FOR NATURAL
RUBBER DIPPING COMPOUNDS (12)

Time (min)	Film deposit thickness (in) *
1	0.017
2	0.023
3	0.027
4	0.030
5	0.033
6	0.035
7	0.038
8	0.040
9	0.043
10	0.045
11	0.048
12	0.050
13	0.052
14	0.054
15	0.056
16	0.058

* Using 545 Coagulant, B.F. Goodrich Co.

for as many as ten times and still retain essential properties (13).

2. *Supported films*

a. For adhesion to metal, coat with "Vulcalock" (B.F. Goodrich C.) adhesive, air dry and dip as above (12).

b. Certain textiles will absorb more latex than others, preliminary tests will determine the rate of build-up.

TABLE 36

RECOMMENDED WASH AND DRY TIME FOR NATURAL
RUBBER DIPPING COMPOUNDS (12)

Film gauge (in)	Wash time (80 F, hrs.)	Dry time (175 F, hrs.)
0.010	1/6	1/2
.015	1/2	1
.020	1/2	1
.025	1/2	1
.030	1	2
.035	2	2
.040	2 1/2	3
.045	3	3
.050	3	3
.055	3	3
.060	3	4
.065	3	4
.070	3	4
.075	3	4
.080	3	4
.090	4	4
.100	5	*

* 4 hours @ 140 F + 6 hours @ 175 F.

Mandrel Coating

Segmented polyurethane polymers such as Biomer (Ethnor Inc.) or Elastomer 753 (Lee Pharmaceuticals) are viscous solutions composed of high concentrations of solvent. Prosthetic tubing of practical wall thicknesses cannot be extruded from the polymer by conventional means since there is no way to remove volatiles during the process. Extrusion of dry granules results in thermal degradation.

To produce high-quality tubing from the polymer, the following effective three-step method is used:

1. Apply polymer to suitable mandrel.
2. Dry to remove solvent.
3. "Heat set" to stabilize desired contours.

This method provides a variety of shapes and sizes to close

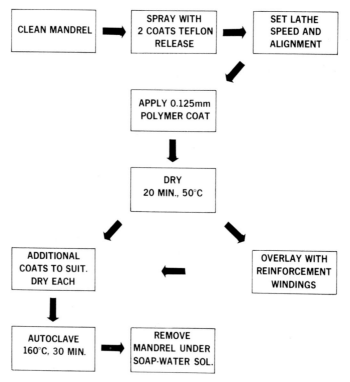

Figure 8. The mandrel coating sequence for segmented polyether urethane.

tolerances with smooth, dense, high gloss surfaces. Figure 8 shows the sequence.

APPLYING THE POLYMER. Suitable mandrels consist of highly polished stainless steel or Teflon reinforced with steel cores. They should be uniformly machined along their lengths for best results.

To apply the polymer, rotate the mandrel in a lathe at slow speeds; meter the polymer onto it in a sequence of layers. Because of its high viscosity, the polymer behaves like a paste, making this means of application possible. To obtain the maximum precision of thickness and smoothness, the polymer is controlled by a flat tool held in position and steadily advanced by the automatic feed mechanism of the lathe. Allow ten minutes of air-drying while the lathe is turning to "set" the polymer firmly in place. Figure 9 shows a second coat being applied to a 12.5 mm diameter mandrel. The finished elastomeric tube is capable of not varying more than 0.025 mm in diameter or wall thickness.

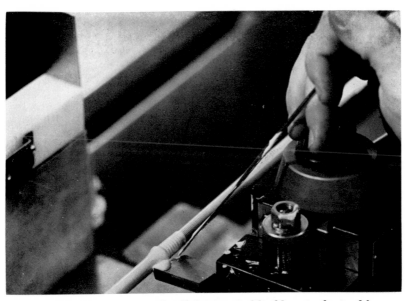

Figure 9. Mandrel coating with a lathe. Desired build-up is obtained by applying repeated coatings. Wire reinforcing windings placed between layers offer resistance to kinking for catheters.

DRYING. Individual coatings, limited to 0.125 mm thickness, are dried twenty minutes at 122 F following each application until the desired build-up is achieved. Successive layers of the polymer are bonded indistinguishably without further preparation of the surfaces. Residual solvent is removed by additional oven-drying for a few hours at 122 F followed by boiling in water.

Removal of tubing from long mandrels is difficult. This operation is best performed by first working a film of detergent solution between the mandrel and the elastomer. After this is done, a strong blast of compressed air will dislodge the tubing and move it along the mandrel. Because of their low coefficient of friction, Teflon mandrels are more easily removed than stainless steel mandrels. The display of elastomeric parts of a heart assist device shown in the upper right hand portion of Figure 10 were molded from segmented polyurethane using this method.

HEAT SETTING. With a slight modification of technique, pros-

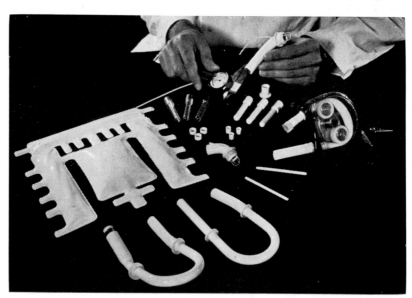

Figure 10. Various shapes and sizes are required for developing a single polymeric device. Precise dimensions, smooth surfaces, as well as close attention to maintenance of optimum physical and physiological properties are necessary.

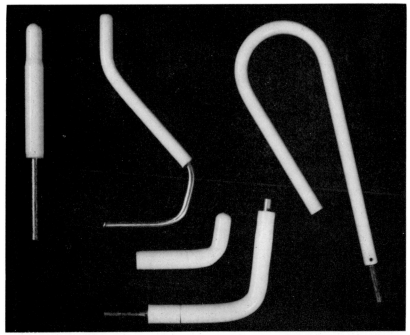

Figure 11. Examples of suitable mandrels for shaping the elastomeric polyurethane. Metal rods are bent and hollow Teflon is pushed over them to provide a non-adherent surface.

thetic tubing with complex contours can be readily produced. Prefabricated straight lengths of the elastomer can be stretched onto curved mandrels having the desired configuration. A stabilized "heat set" is achieved after thirty minutes in an oven or a steam vulcanizer at 320 F. Figure 11 shows some typical curved Teflon mandrels that are reinforced with metal rods. Figure 12 shows elastomeric prostheses that were "heat set" on these mandrels and then removed after cooling. Again, detergent and air pressure assist in removal (14, 15).

Painting

Polyvinyl chloride plastisols and silicone rubber are suitable for painting onto molds made for maxillofacial prostheses. (*See* flexible mold materials, Ch. IV.)

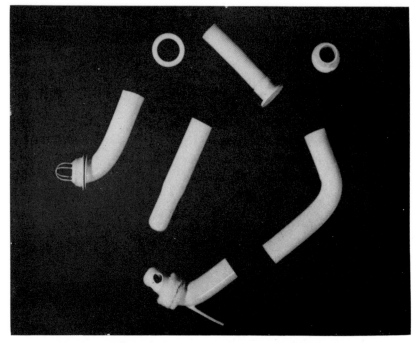

Figure 12. Shaped elastomeric tubes after being "heat set."

Gross pathological specimens can be replicated in a life-like fashion through procedures developed by Peck and co-workers (16). A lead metal mold is made of the specimen through casting techniques and the pigmented vinyl plastisol is painted onto the surface by means of a camel's hair brush to achieve the desired build-up. The mold is kept at 212 F by passing it, occasionally, through the flame of a Bunsen burner; the heat fuses the plastisol. After the final coat, the vinyl is cured in a dry heat oven at 356 F for four minutes. The method permits delayed examination of pathologic tissue without histological distortion, according to the developers.

Tinting maxillofacial prostheses of silicone rubber has been developed by Firtell and Bartlett (17) by mixing earth pigments and liquid RTV silicone rubber to produce basic colors. The rubber paints are vulcanized by using an overspray of catalyst and allowing the coating to set for twelve to eighteen hours. Proportions of catalyst used follow those recommended by the manufacturers of the silicone rubber (Silicure, General Electric Co.).

Bartlett, Pinead and Moore (18) have tinted maxillofacial prostheses made from silicone rubber by thinning an RTV silicone adhesive (Medical Silicone Adhesive Type A, Dow Corning Corp.) to the consistency of paint. This is accomplished by using equal parts of silicone adhesive and xylene. Small amounts of inorganic pigment are added to individual batches of the adhesive mixture to achieve the desired assortment of colors; the adhesive paint is applied with a cotton swab. A complete cure of the coating is obtained through the inherent curing mechanism of the adhesive.

HAND LAY-UP METHOD. The fiberglass-epoxy hand lay-up method is well known for ease, versatility and strength of structural units which can be produced by it. A thixotropic paste of epoxy, or gel coat, is painted onto a suitable form; sequential layers of fiberglass cloth and a thin laminating resin are applied until the object takes form. Figures 13, A, B, and C, show a fiberglass-epoxy, monkey-restraining chair being constructed from a commercially available resin system (Hysol RT laminating resin system, Hysol Corp.).

Silicone rubber, heat vulcanizing stocks (*see* silicone rubber, Ch. I) can be formed using the hand lay-up method. Complicated shapes such as might be presented with a heart ventricle of an artificial heart are good examples. Sheets of the material are carefully laid over the form and pressed together at points of contact; the uncured material will bond well to itself during vulcanization. Topaz (19) has described this method of molding artificial hearts. The heart form is cast into shape using a 150 F melting wax which is polished to a high gloss by rubbing with a soft cloth and combinations of acetone and ether. A barrier coating of either polymethyl methacrylate, soap, polyvinyl alcohol, shellac or varnish is applied to the wax to obviate any possible reaction between the form and the rubber. Dacron reinforced raw sheets of silicone rubber, obtained by calendering (available, Dow Corning Corp.) heat vulcanizing silicone rubber stock, are shaped over the mold. The assembly is autoclaved at 270 F for five minutes; the presence of the rubber on the out-

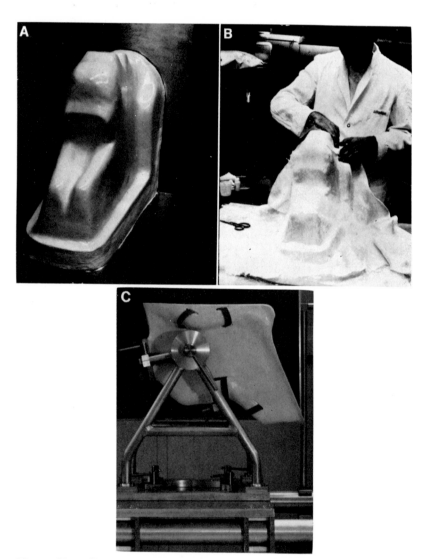

Figure 13. A fiberglass restraining chair for monkeys by means of the hand lay-up method. (A) The form with hard wax surface. (B) Laying-up the fiberglass-epoxy sequentially. (C) The finished chair with molded-in bolts for securing to frame.

side of the wax insulates it from the heat until the rubber is firm. The silicone rubber is oven cured at 350 F for four hours; the wax is allowed to flow from the core and is collected.

Kessler and co-workers (20) have used low melting polyethylene (Epolene C-10, Tennessee Eastman Co., Inc.) for their molds and recommend slicing the edges of the rubber on a bevel to produce smooth junctions before laying against the mold. Joints which are smooth and uniform are important when used in the vascular system and minimize clotting.

Electrophoresis of Polymers

Just as metal can be electroplated from solution by the passage of an electric current, so may lattices of polymers such as natural rubber, phenol formaldehyde, polyvinylidene chloride and others. As long as the latex particle is negatively charged it will migrate, under the influence of an electric current, towards its anode to build-up any desired deposit. Anodes are best made from highly positive valence structure materials such as zinc, nickel or iron. These positive ions react with and are taken into solution by the hydroxyl ions of electrolysis and thereby prevent gassing at the opposite electrode. The polymer on the metal remains porous throughout the process, allowing fresh ions to be renewed at the other surface. Alkalinity and conductivity must be carefully controlled so not to upset the ion balance (21). Figure 14 shows a typical arrangement for electrodepositing polymers.

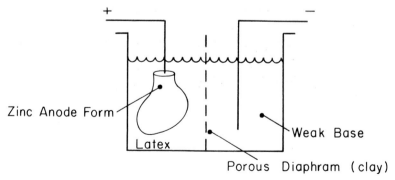

Figure 14. Electrophoresis of polymeric latex to produce complex shapes.

Natural rubber products were produced in England for many years under this anode process. A typical bath is made by adding 500 g of rubber latex (30% dry rubber content) to 10 g of a 15% solution of a stabilizer (Vulcastab L.S., Vanderbilt Rubber Co., or equal) while the latex is stirred. To this, add 20 g of an accelerator such as sodium n,n,-diethyldithio-carbamate and 5 g of sulfur. The solid content of the mixture is then adjusted to 15% by volume with the addition of distilled water. Zinc oxide or carbon black could also be used as a filler (22). Once the desired deposit is achieved, the rubber is dried and cured. Natural rubber made in this fashion has higher tensile strength than does milled rubber.

Phenol formaldehyde can be electrodeposited in a manner similar to that used for natural rubber. Thicknesses up to 0.100 inch can be readily obtained from suspensions of Bakelite (Union Carbide Corp.) in water or oil and modifiers. Similarly, cellulose can be dissolved in zinc chloride or cuprammonium solution and electrodeposited at the anode using a current density of 75 amp/square foot at 110 volts. Be careful!

Foaming

Sponges of silicone rubber and polyurethane have played an important role in medical research. Sponges can be either open-cell, closed-cell, rigid or flexible. Although the chemical components, to a large degree, determine their characteristics, the method of fabrication is also contributory. Silicone sponges can be heat vulcanizing or room temperature vulcanizing. Closed-cell sponge made from heat vulcanizing stocks have been used for facial tissue substitutes, temporary supports to augment and realign tissue, and as plombage following thoractomies. The sponge can be bonded to itself or to Dacron, etched Teflon, polymethyl methacrylate and metals by using Silastic Medical Adhesive Type A (*see* adhesives, Ch. V).

Closed-cell sponge is somewhat difficult to produce. A typical procedure is as follows (23):

1. Mix Silastic stock on tightly set mill. (*See* compounding, Ch. II.)
2. Add a blowing agent, typically 3% Nitrosan BL 353

(N,N'-dimethyl, N,N'-dinitrosoterephthalamide) and dis-
perse thoroughly.

3. Shelf age several days.
4. Remill and pack tightly in mold.
5. Cold press several times, trimming off excess each time
   until all air is removed.
6. Press mold, three minutes forty-five seconds to four minutes at 250 F. Time is critical as stock may not sponge or
   will remain raw.

Some destruction of cell structure to produce a semiclosed condition can be achieved by crushing between the rolls of a mill.

Open cell sponge is easier to produce than the closed-cell
material but is considerably weaker. Silastic S-5370 RTV foam
(Silastic 386, Dow Corning Corp.), a thick fluid, is mixed with
its catalyst-blowing agent and stirred vigorously for thirty
seconds and allowed to expand. Within five minutes, the material vulcanizes to a light, rubbery, brown foam. To prevent
collapse of the sponge, it must be allowed to develop full strength
by curing, undisturbed, at room temperature for twenty-four
hours.

For both types of sponge described above, a thorough washing to remove residues is required before they can be used in
the body. Both materials can be readily cut to the shape of the
desired implant. Boucher (24) has used it for rebuilding the
alveolar ridge in edentulous patients.

Flexible polyurethane foam was once used for molding leaflets of artificial heart valves (4). Rigid polyurethane was used
as a bone cement (25). Both materials have fallen from use
because of inadequate strength.

Pressure Molding

Compression, injection and transfer molding are used to
shape compounds under heat and pressure.

Compression Molding

Compression molding is the most frequently used molding
method and is applicable to large items and many shapes. While
most compression molding is restricted to thermosetting ma-

terials, which undergo both physical and chemical changes, thermoplastics can also be used. Compression molding is generally avoided if dimensions at the parting line between the two halves of the mold must be precise or if the amount of flash remaining on the part is of major consideration. Flash is difficult to eliminate altogether but can be reduced by narrowing the land area immediately adjacent to the mold cavity to $\frac{1}{16}$ to $\frac{1}{4}$ inch, depending on the size of the mold and the clamping pressure used. Allowance should be made for venting. This can be accomplished by designing the mold so that it splits at undercuts and sharp corners; blind holes should never be incorporated into the mold. Slight scratches along the abutting faces of the mold can serve to bleed off entrapped air. In the case of silicone rubber, quick release of pressure shortly after the rubber has filled the mold also helps release air. Hollow objects can be molded using core pins or inserts built into the mold. (*See*

Figure 15. Compression mold design. Note use of core pin (center) and narrow land areas on left face of mold adjacent to cavity.

Fig. 15.) The following are the other considerations when molding rubber:

1. *Thick sections.* Most rubber can be cured in thicknesses up to $\frac{1}{4}$ inch without special precautions; thicker sections are limited to special compounds and curing schedules.

2. *Overcure.* Do not overcure; choose the minimum cure for the desired properties.

3. *Inserts.* Special primers must be used for adhering rubber to metal. Inserts of metal can reinforce the part, permit attachment of other parts or maintain the shape of the rubber.

4. *Holes.* Holes are best molded in-place. Rubber is subject to tearing if inadvertently cut longitudinally. Holes less than $\frac{1}{8}$ inch should not be attempted unless short in length. The recommended ratio of stock thickness to insert pin diameter is 6:1.

5. *Design.* Keep the design simple. Where possible, eliminate intricate projections, undercuts and shapes which may lend to tearing, or poor molding.

6. *Shrinkage.* All elastomers shrink while being molded. The degree of shrinkage can only be generally estimated until actual experience with the shape sets the limits.

7. *Sharp corners.* Sharp corners not only make molds difficult to machine but add problems to filling the mold completely.

Injection Molding

Thermoplastic polymers are heated to a molten state and forced under pressure into a relatively cool mold, where it solidifies to form the object; for example, syringes, poppets for heart valves, dentures, contact lenses, artificial eyes and contraceptive devices. Molds contain a series of channels which evenly distribute the molten polymer to the cavity. Figure 16 shows a typical arrangement.

This type of molding is most applicable with intricate shapes and tight tolerances. Thermoplastics, fast-curing elastomers and thermosetting resins can be injection molded; only a limited number of cavities are necessary for high volume work because the molding cycle is usually short.

Injection molding machines are available in different sizes. They can be operated either manually, semiautomatically or automatically. They are rated in size by the quantity of material which can be injected in one cycle, ranging from a fraction of an ounce in small laboratory models to several pounds in large production machines.

Basically, the injection press consists of two units—one for opening and closing the mold and one for injecting the plastic. The first half consists of a hydraulic or toggle-operated moving platen and a stationary platen. The mold halves are fastened securely to these platens. The second half is made up of a feed hopper, a controlled feeding device, a heated injection cylinder and an injection plunger. Figure 17 shows an open mold, the press and polymethyl methacrylate being molded.

Most thermoplastics are supplied by the manufacturers in various formulas to provide the most efficient production as well as the most desirable properties in the finished product; plastic must have good flow properties to be injection molded. Flow, as related to injection molding, is the amount of travel a plastic material undergoes when subjected to heat and pressure.

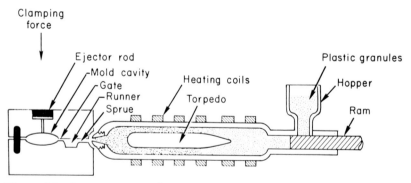

Figure 16. Cutaway view of injection machine. Plastic granules are fed from a hopper to a hydraulically operated ram, which forces granules into a heated chamber. Once the molten plastic reaches the nozzle, it is forced with each advance of the ram into the mold cavity where it solidifies on cooling.

Figure 17. A typical small injection molding press. The temperature of the open mold is controlled by means of the interconnecting oil bath on the left. Timing cycles control the molding conditions.

Thermoplastics absorb moisture from the atmosphere by the combined effects of temperature and relative humidity. Because of this, good practice dictates drying of the molding pellets immediately prior to use to obtain pieces free of moisture bubbles, surface imperfections and to maintain uniform flow. Drying can usually be accomplished by heating the pellets for two to four hours at 140 to 170 F depending upon the temperature limitations of the plastic.

In designing a part for injection molding, the following should be considered and included if possible:

1. Large flat areas of the plastic part should be reinforced with ribs.
2. In order to prevent sink marks on the surface opposite ribs, the wall thickness of the ribs should not be greater than approximately 75 percent of the wall thickness of the surface which they reinforce.
3. External corners should be rounded whenever possible, except at the mold parting lines.
4. Sharp internal corners usually cause strains in the molded piece, so radii or fillets should be provided.
5. Avoid undercuts and abrupt changes in thickness and in cross section.
6. Adequate draft should be provided to facilitate ejection from the mold; two to five degrees is preferred.
7. Allow for shrinkage.

Typical molding difficulties often encountered and their suggested solution:

1. *Incomplete or short-molded pieces.* The mold or resin is too cold if the pressure is reasonably high.
2. *The mold flashes.* Due to overheating or injection pressure too great.
3. *Sink or shrink marks.* The material is too hot or the gates are incorrectly located.
4. *Surface lamination.* Caused by contamination or lack of pressure and heat.
5. *Poor welds or flow marks.* Material too cold or pressure too low.
6. *Bubbles in the interior.* Improper venting causes trapped air/moisture in material.
7. *Brittleness.* Material was overheated and decomposed.
8. *Pieces stick to cavity.* Undercuts or insufficient draft, poorly polished surfaces or removed from mold too soon.
9. *Pieces warp after removal from cavity.* Heavy sections of plastic distort on standing if still hot.
10. *Cloudy appearance.* Moisture in material or contamination.
11. *Scorching or molded pieces have odor.* Material too hot or contains trapped air.

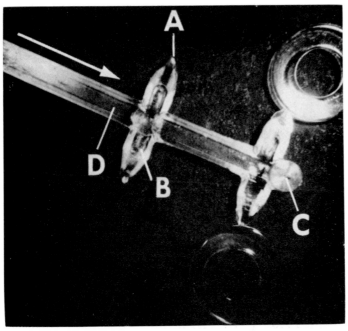

Figure 18. Sprue, runner, gate, and cold-slug design for best injection mold-ing technique. Acrylic disks for tissue pathology studies. $(A) =$ gate, $(B) =$ runner, $(C) =$ cold slug, $(D) =$ sprue. Arrow indicates direction of flow.

General measures used to keep molding difficulties to a minimum:

1. Use a cold slug cavity at the end of the sprue to catch any cold polymer; design it larger in diameter than the sprue. (*See* Fig. 18.)
2. Runners which are used to carry the plastic to the cavity should be designed to have the largest possible cross section; a trapezoid shape is ideal.
3. Gates, which are immediately adjacent to the cavity and prevent backing-out of the plastic, should be straight and located on heavy sections. The thickness of the gate should be 40 to 60 percent as thick as the section of the cavity at which the gate is located. Thickness of a re-stricted gate should not exceed .075 inch. Length of gates have a direct effect on resistance to flow. This can be

used to equalize the flow into several cavities by giving them gates of different lengths.

4. Use a flat groove .002 to .008 inch deep and ⅛ to ¼ inch wide to vent air and locate it opposite the gate.

5. Ejector pins. Holes to accomodate pins should be relieved .002 to .005 inch up to within a fraction of an inch of the face of the cavity. Provide a clearance of 1/64 to 1/32 inch around the heads of pins. This will allow for slight misalignment between the holes in the cavity plate and the ejector pins. Chamfer all holes where ejector pins will enter the mold.

6. Adjust temperature and injection pressure.

Custom molding of polymethyl methacrylate ocular prostheses represents a variation of injection molding. The technique is an outgrowth of a need for a life-like eye that would move in coordination with an existing eye and offer the greatest degree of comfort, permanence and esthetics to the patient. The custom acrylic molded eye replaced ready-made glass and plastic eyes in the late 1940's (26). The method consists of the following steps:

1. Obtaining an accurate impression of the enucleated area using alginate impression material. (*See* mold materials, Ch. IV.)

2. Making the basic pattern from wax.

3. Molding of the prosthesis using pigmented methyl methacrylate. This part of the process deviates from conventional prosthetic dentistry. A wax pattern of the desired eye is made from the alginate impression. A wax sprue is attached to the corneal area and both are invested in two halves with dental stone (Ranson & Randolph Co.) using a conventional brass dental injection flask. A coil of small copper tubing is soldered around the injection plunger barrel and the existing hole in the flask lid is enlarged to 15 mm and notched to pass the coil-cylinder assembly. It is important that the cylinder be embedded in the stone to evenly transfer heat and prevent galling of the plunger. Thus prepared, the mold is opened and the wax flushed away with hot water. All

surfaces are mold-released with sodium silicate and the flask reassembled. (*See* Fig. 19.)

A mixture of monomer and pigmented polymer of methyl methacrylate is prepared according to the manufacturers (L.D. Caulk Co.) suggested ratios and is packed into the upper and lower sections using a clean spatula. It is important to prevent the inclusion of dirt and moisture during the packing process in order to prevent clouding, bubbling or crazing of the polymer. Underpacking will eliminate excess "flash" between the two halves of the mold. The flask is securely locked together, the cylinder partially filled and the plunger placed in position. A spring pressure jack is used to exert a downward force on the plunger to drive the resin into the mold cavity as it liquifies. In order to obtain the best results with the resin, the flask should be half-way submerged in a room temperature water bath and the temperature advanced at a rate of 1.8 F per minute until the water boils. The water in the cooling coil is closed off and the flask is allowed to dwell in the hot water for thirty minutes

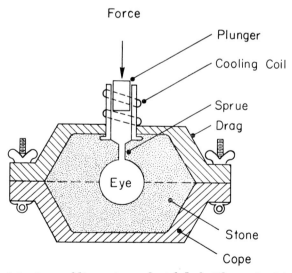

Figure 19. Injection molding using a dental flask. The entire injection flask assembly showing the position of the pattern, the sprue and the method of injecting methyl methacrylate monomer-polymer resin under slow and constant pressure.

followed by a fifteen-minute soak in cold water. The mold is opened and the stone broken away. The sprue is cut off and the prosthesis is polished with felt cones and brushes; for a very high polish, wet whiting can be used. (*See* machining of plastics, Ch. VI.)

The iris is painted onto a disc of paper and inserted at the proper location, into a counterbored recess in the acrylic eye, and reinvested in stone. Clear methyl methacrylate is reinjected into the area and finished as above to complete the process.

Sheldon and Pudenze (27) have used a compression molding method similar to this for making transparent calvariums to visually observe the brain of experimental animals. An impression of the bony defect is obtained, casts and molds are fashioned, and the clear acrylic is molded. The methyl methacrylate liquid monomer and powdered polymer are mixed by adding three parts of powder to one part of liquid and allowing the mix to stand for ten minutes.

The mold is preheated to 150 F and the jelly-like mixture is packed carefully within the mold cavity. The mold is closed and clamped tightly together. It is placed in a boiling water bath for forty-five minutes and then slowly cooled to room temperature; the finished piece is removed and polished.

Transfer Molding

A predetermined amount of thermosetting polymer is heated in a separate chamber and forced by a ram into a hot mold cavity for curing. This method is similar to compression molding except it offers greater control of thickness of the part, minimizes flash at parting lines, and can more readily accommodate inserts. Figure 20 shows a transfer mold for an anesthesia mask of complex shape.

Extruding

Polymers may be forced through a shaped orifice to form continuous lengths with uniform cross section. (*See* Fig. 21). Some extruders will accommodate either plastic or rubber by using an appropriate mechanical screw advance driven by a large horsepower motor, a cross-head feed, and water-cooled

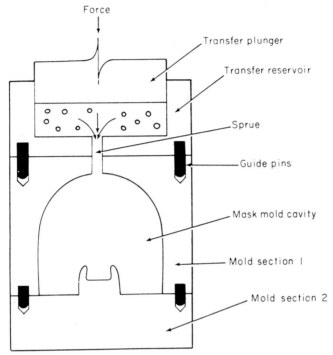

Figure 20. Sagittal section of a typical transfer mold. Rubber is forced from the reservoir into the mold cavity. The transfer reservoir may be optionally removed and the mold pressed between heated platens for the duration of cure.

and electrically heated barrels with temperature regulators. Rubber and thermoplastics differ markedly in the conditions required to extrude rod, tubes or wire insulation. Thermoplastics must be heated to their melting temperatures to force them through an extruder; rubbers must be softened with heat to achieve adequate flow, whereas silicone rubber is generally extruded at room temperature to prevent premature vulcanization.

Screw dimensions also vary for each material. In Figure 22 the uppermost screw, designed for extruding silicone rubber, has a much deeper root diameter than the other screw which is designed for extruding thermoplastics. Vascular implants, catheters, vascular shunts, blood collection and administration sets, and sutures have been made in this fashion.

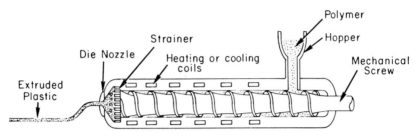

Figure 21. Cutaway section of typical extruder. The polymer is fed from a hopper to a mechanical screw which forces the material through a heating or cooling area, an air and particle strainer, and the die nozzle which gives it shape. From this point it is conveyed by belt to a water bath or curing oven from where it emerges as the finished product.

The type of mechanical devices for holding and centering the cores and dies is of great importance. Many die dimensions are arrived at empirically because of the difficulty in predicting such variables as die swell in relation to speed, size of extrusion and type of material.

A convenient and low-cost method for extruding hot-vulcanizing stocks of silicone rubber, or other soft materials, is to use a plunger-and-cylinder arrangement similar to that shown in Figure 23. Here a continuous coating is being applied to a coil spring which will be used as cardiac pacemaker electrodes (28). By regulating the tension on the spring and the speed through

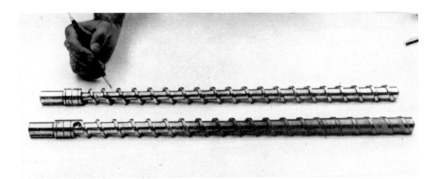

Figure 22. Two extruder screws, rubber vs plastic. The top screw is for rubber; the bottom screw is for plastic. Note the difference in root diameters.

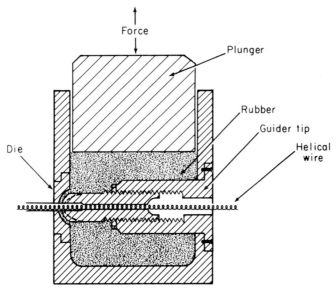

Figure 23. A plunger-and-cylinder arrangement for extruding silicone rubber onto coiled wire.

the unit, the coil can be externally coated only or the rubber can be allowed to enter the coil and completely encapsulate it. The method is limited by the size of the reservoir chamber and the amount of rubber it will hold.

Rotational Molding

Rotational molding is also called rotomolding or rotocasting and differs from other techniques such as blow and injection molding by the following: (a) hollow items of any size or shape (or solid) can be readily made and (b) the resin melts in the mold and does not require a driving pressure.

In rotational molding, rigid or resilient hollow bodies are formed from powdered plastic materials or vinyl plastisols by being heated and rotated simultaneously in two planes perpendicular to each other. The plastic particles contact, melt or fuse, as the case may be, on the inner surfaces of the hot molds and build up in thickness until all the material is fused and the finished product if formed.

Of special mention is the fact that rotationally molded pieces are stress-free, except for slight shrinkage forces, because the pieces are produced without uneven pressure. Highly stress-crack resistant objects have been rotomolded using cross-linkable polyethylene (29).

Blow Molding

The earliest known application of blow molding dates back to an 1851 patent for forming objects of gutta-percha, a form of natural rubber. Since then, a great number of variations have developed. Basically, the method consists of heating a hollow tube of a particular plastic to its softening point (*see* melting temperatures, Ch. VI), clamping it between the faces of a cold mold and forcing high-pressure water or air through a needle which pierces the plastic. The hot plastic is expanded against the cavity of the mold and allowed to cool, in place. Once cool, the mold is opened and the hollow article removed. For objects requiring that they be completely closed—that is, no needle puncture—charges of gas-generating substances can be placed inside the tubing to expand on heating and form the cavity.

Another variation is to clamp cold sheets of plastic between the mold and heat until the plastic softens before blowing. A "serum cell" having inlet and outlet ports is an example. Two wafers of polyethylene film and two pieces of polyethylene tubing mounted on hypodermic needles are inserted into the mold and the mold is closed. One of the stainless steel needles is sealed off. The mold is heated to 180 F while being clamped at 100 psi in a laboratory press. After five minutes of heating, the wafers are inflated with 20 psi of air through the second hypodermic needle. The mold is cooled to room temperature and the hollow polyethylene cell removed. Complete fusion of the two wafers occurs along the edges and they are permanently welded to the polyethylene tubing. Upon removal of the stainless steel needles, the cells are ready for use.

Gaertner (30) has described an intravascular catheter of Teflon which retains its position within blood vessels by means of molded enlargements extending outward from the walls of the tubing. These ballooned areas are formed by placing 0.052 by 0.028 inch Teflon tubing in a two-part symmetrical brass mold

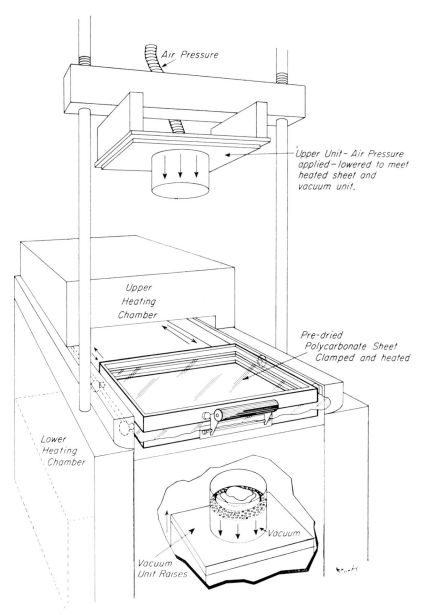

Figure 24. A typical vacuum-forming arrangement.

with the intended shape machined therein. A 20-gauge needle is inserted into one end of the tubing and the mold assembly is heated to 600 F. (Care must be taken to assure that exactly this temperature is obtained.) Pressure is then applied by way of a 10-cc syringe attached to the exposed needle expanding the soft Teflon against the inside configuration of the mold. While maintaining pressure through the syringe, the mold is cooled to room temperature with cold water; the new shape is set.

Thermoforming

Vacuum and/or pressure may be used to conform a heated plastic sheet to the shape of a solid mold. The plastic sheet is heated to a compliant state, then securely placed over a sealed

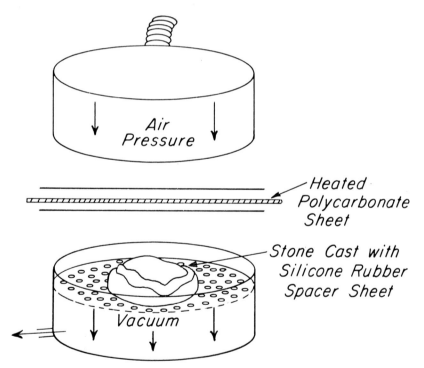

Figure 25. A polycarbonate film being thermoformed over a gypsum mold. Here, additional assistance is provided by a positive pressure chamber attached to the upper platen.

chamber containing the mold. Vacuum is maintained in a reservoir tank which, when opened, draws the hot plastic over the mold. Figures 24 and 25 show a typical thermoforming operation in which a prosthesis for cranioplasty is being formed (31).

Others

Tapering of Teflon tubing can be accomplished by applying a hemostat to both ends of tubing and heating two to three inches in length over a gas flame until the tube becomes opaque. Do not allow the tubing to overheat, as indicated by becoming clear. Remove the tubing from the flame and pull in opposite directions until the amount of stretching necessary to produce the desired taper is accomplished. Plunge the tubing into cold water to cool and set. Flaring of tubing ends can be done in a similar fashion by inserting a stainless steel mandrel, having the desired flare, into the lumen of the hot Teflon and holding it there until it cools (30).

Polyethylene can be heat formed to produce tapered tubing. The polyethylene tubing is heated over a hot air gun until it becomes clear. Any angle and any degree of taper can be achieved by uniform pulling followed by chilling the polyethylene.

Ore, Sebestyen and Stone (32) have prepared shaped lengths of tubing to be used as glaucoma drains made from straight lengths of silicone rubber tubing. This method of forming reorients the molecular bonds between the polymerized siloxane chains to a new configuration which if not carefully executed will severely disturb the normal structure of the rubber resulting in poor elongation and tear strength of the rubber. For this reason, this technic is not recommended for general use.

A basic equipment complement necessary to perform all the aforementioned methods of molding, regardless of the size of the facility or the number of personnel, is suggested below:

A well equipped facility requires about 2000 sq. ft. It should be air-conditioned and equipped with separate exhaust hoods over presses, mills or any other equipment giving off chemical vapors.

Useful Plastics Machinery

Calender
Dielectric sealer (RF)
Hot air gun, 1000 F
Injection molder, 1½ oz., 18-ton, 600 F maximum
Plastic welding torch, 700 F maximum
Thermoformer, 14″ x 20″, dual platens and heaters

Useful Rubber Machinery

Extruder, 1″ diameter capacity, 800 F maximum, water cooling jacket, length to diameter ratio 2.35:1, 2 hp with 8:1 speed change
Hydraulic press, 30-ton, 10″ × 10″, 650 F maximum
Oven, 650 F maximum, horizontal airflow, 19″ × 19″ × 19″
Roll mill, 6″ diameter × 13″, 7½ hp with reversing starter, roll friction ratio of 1.3:1 with 24 rpm on fast roll. Hollow bored rolls for circulating coolant or heat.
Steam vulcanizer, 24″ × 36″, 0 to 35 psi, minimum

Others

Gauges, handtools, glassware
Lathe, 14″ variable speed, 2 hp
Refrigerator, explosion-proof
Surface pyrometer, 400 F

MOLDING MATERIALS

Molds can be constructed from metal, rubber, plastic or gypsum depending upon the type of molding elected. Metal molds are necessary with high pressures, rubber or plastic can accommodate casting materials with deep undercuts and gypsum is advantageous for low-pressure molding. Each of these has individual value depending upon the circumstance.

Metal Molds

Molds for pressure molding can be made from aluminum, brass, steel, stainless steel, beryllium copper or other durable metals. Most molds are subject to severe punishment and localized stresses, especially if pressures are high and subject to repeated cyclic loading. Platen faces and mold plates may not be flat and parallel or the mold design may concentrate stress. Further, the polymer to be processed or its additives may cause corrosion or pitting shortening the useful life of a particular metal. For instance, polyvinyl chloride may be molded in aluminum molds for short runs and simple shapes, however, unless the mold is made from stainless steel or chrome-plated steel, surface corrosion over an extended period of time will interfer with the production of smooth stress-free surfaces on the molded piece.

Steel

All steel deforms slightly when loaded or stressed and returns to shape only if elastic limit is not exceeded. The higher the elastic limit and hardness of a particular grade of steel, the higher will be its load carrying capacity. Two grades are commonly used, a medium carbon steel with a Brinell hardness of 165–185 and an SAE 6145 electric furnace grade with a Brinell hardness of 225. The former is more easily machined and produces smoother cuts, whereas the latter is used where it is necessary to build long life into the mold and to minimize damage to parting line surfaces.

Beryllium Copper

Barsoum and El-Ebrahi (33) have used a technique for the construction of tooth molds made of beryllium-copper alloy. They point out that beryllium-copper alloys can be treated to levels of hardness and strength approaching those of steel. The melting range for beryllium-copper alloys is 1600 to 1780 F and they are often centrifugally cast.

Low Melting Alloys

Low temperature melting alloys of bismuth are ideal for rapid and accurate production of individual or multiple cavity molds. Fine detail and high luster surface finishes equaling the master model can be obtained when cast against metal, gypsum, wood, ceramic and plastics.

Bismuth is a heavy, coarse crystalline metal which expands 3.3 percent of its volume when it solidifies from the molten state. This expansion can be controlled, however, by alloying with metals such as lead, tin or cadmium. Table 37 lists a number of the better known eutectic alloys, their composition and melting points. A number of non-eutectic alloys exist having a temperature range of from 142 to 338 F.

Cerrocast® is the alloy most often used for close tolerance work. It expands only slightly during casting and cooling, with

TABLE 37

EUTECTIC ALLOYS

Alloy	Bi	Composition (%) Pb	Sn	Cd	Approximate Melting Point (F)
Cerrotru *	58	—	42	—	281
Cerrobase *	55.5	44.5	—	—	255
Cerrobend *	50	26.7	13.3	10	158
D'Arcet metal	50	25	25	—	199
Lipowitz's metal	50	27	13	10	158
Newton's metal	50	31	19	—	203
Rose's alloy	50	28	22	—	212
Wood's alloy	50	24	14	12	160
Wood's metal	50	25	12.5	12.5	160

Hardness of fusible alloys ranges from 5 to 22 Brinell, tensile strength from 3,000 to 13,000 psi and elongation from 1% to 300%.

* The Cerro Sales Corp.
Note: Not intended for implants.

minimal "shrinkage." Measurements taken at one-hour and 24-hour periods after the casting reached room temperature showed excellent dimensional stability with a maximum increase of 0.0001 inch variation from an original test bar of ½ by ½ by 10 inches.

Meltable cores of Cerrotru have been used in molding sections of prosthetic heart chambers (34). In this case, the core was firmly mounted between the two halves of an aluminum outer shell and clamped in a platen press. Medical grade silicone rubber was transferred into the mold cavity and around the core. The rubber was cured at 225 to 250 F for ten minutes. The mold was opened and the alloy core removed from the firmly set rubber by melting in a hotter oven. The method is reported to offer the advantage of producing numerous hollow-rubber prostheses while maintaining a smooth and accurate finish.

Metallizing of Molds

Molds can be made by electroforming over disposable cores or mandrels to form unique shapes and contours such as occur in heart chambers and other vascular devices. Paper, plastic, plaster and wax can be used as these cores with removal, afterwards, by melting or acid etching. Methods for making surfaces conductive and susceptible to electroforming are (a) incorporation of a conductive filler into the surface layer of the nonconductor, (b) painting conductive lacquers, (c) evaporating metal particles under vacuum and (d) chemical precipitation of metals. Subsequent brush plating of these surfaces can increase durability.

Conductive Fillers

Conductive fillers include graphite and metallic powders of copper and silver. These can be incorporated into plastic, rubber or wax molding mixes or sprinkled onto the surface of the mold so that particles adhere when subjected to heat and/or pressure.

GRAPHITE. Once a uniform coating of graphite is achieved, fine iron filings are brushed onto the surface, followed by a dip coating of copper from a standard copper sulfate plating bath or by brush plating. The iron particles act as a cathode and the graphite as an anode, thereby causing the copper to deposit on the graphite and fill in any gaps between individual particles. Residual iron is then washed from the surface and the object is further processed by electroforming. (*See* electroforming, Ch. IV.)

COPPER. Copper can be incorporated into surfaces in a similar manner to graphite. The object is then brushed with fine zinc powder and immersed in a silver cyanide plating bath to uniformly deposit silver. Only a quick dip is advisable since cyanide in the bath may dissolve areas of the copper surface Practice is required.

SILVER. Silver particles suspended in plastics, such as epoxies and vinyls (Technical Wire Products, Inc., Emerson and Cummings Inc., Electrofilm Inc., J. Walman and Sons), which have volume resistivities of 0.001 ohm-cms, need no additional treatment but can be plated directly.

Silicone rubber RTV molds can be made conductive by wrapping with a metal wire electrode and dusting the surface of the rubber with a flake-like copper or silver powder (35). Rubbing of the surface with a camel's hair brush forces the particles into good contact with the rubber. Flooding of the surface with a stream of water orients the flakes into a thin, lapped layer having good conductivity for plating.

Painting of Conductive Lacquers

This is the simplest and one of the most reliable means of preparing nonconductive surfaces for plating. Although conductive paints of copper, gold, platinum, palladium (Electrochemicals Dept. E.I. du Pont de Nemours and Co., Inc.) and zinc are used, silver paint having 60% to 70% metal pigment is best for most situations. Many lacquer formulations consist of about 1 fluid ounce of nitrocellulose lacquer, 7 fluid ounces of lacquer thinner, and 2 ounces of metal lining powder. Cellulosic ester, methacrylate and epoxy type resins are also used as binders.

Vacuum Metallizing

This method of metallizing surfaces is performed by heating a metal to its vaporization point while under vacuum. Coatings deposited in this fashion are generally in the order of several angstroms thickness and require considerable skill and control to subsequently build up by electroplating. Also, temperature sensitive plastics can melt if placed too close to the electrode or others can outgas resulting in blistered surfaces.

Chemical Precipitation

Metallic coatings of copper, silver and gold (Shipley Co., Inc.) can be achieved on nonconductors by chemical precipitation.

These deposits are more homogenous in structure than those laid down by other means because of the crystal growth which occurs. Mirrors have been "silvered" in this manner for many years. The process consists of "sensitizing" the nonconductor, and reducing silver onto it. First, roughen the surface to enhance adhesion of the deposit, then treat as follows:

1. Sensitize by immersing in a mixture of

Stannous chloride	10 g
Hydrochloric acid	40 g
Water	1 liter

   This treatment promotes adhesion of the silver precipitate onto the surface and is essential to the technique.

2. Rinse well in distilled water.

3. Make up two solutions described below and add one part of reducer solution A to four parts of silver solution B at 68 F and pour over the object to be coated.

   A. Reducer:

Cane sugar	90 g
Nitric acid	4 ml
Distilled water	1 liter
Boil and cool before using.	

   B. Silver solution:

Silver nitrate	20 g
Potassium hydroxide	10 g
Distilled water	400 ml
Ammonium hydroxide	50 cc

Ammonium hydroxide is added to keep the silver in solution. Do not add silver solution ingredients in a concentrated form or allow them to dry as a violent reaction can occur.

Brush Plating

Occasionally the nature of a mold or mandrel dictates that it be made from brass, copper or electroformed metal and then electroplated to achieve a hard and corrosion resistant surface. For these situations brushed plating can serve a necessary function. Brush plating, although impractical on a commercial basis, lends itself well to single applications. Aside from being more convenient for the small laboratory, it has the decided advantages of being able to uniformly coat recessed areas and to produce a finish that is several times less porous than obtained by regular plating procedures.

A simple brush applicator can be made from a nylon brush with a stainless steel wire embedded into the bristles as the positive electrode. Highly viscous electrolytes are needed to keep the brush saturated. Two typical formulations are as follows:

Nickel Plating

Boric acid	10 g
Nickel sulfate	60 g
Potassium bitartrate	10 g
Water	1 liter

Dissolve the nickel sulfate, potassium bitartrate and boric acid in hot water. Add a 70 to 30 mixture of glycerine and carbowax to give a thin paste.
Current density: 10 to 25 amps/sq. ft.
Voltage: 3 volts

Gold Plating

Gold potassium cyanide	5 g
Disodium phosphate	20 g
Sodium cyanide	5 g
Water	1 liter

Add the phosphate and cyanide complexes to the water followed by the gold potassium cyanide. Add a 90 to 10 mixture of calcium carbonate and glycerine to produce a thin paste. Current density and voltage similar to that for nickel plating.

Hydraulic brush plating can be achieved by using conventional electroplating solutions in conjunction with a hydraulic applicator. Figure 26 shows such a device.

Electroforming

Electroforming is the process of building heavy metal deposits onto structural shapes by way of electrolytic means. Quite often, this technique can be used to fabricate complex shapes which would be extremely costly or difficult to produce by any other method. Outstanding examples of this are phonograph

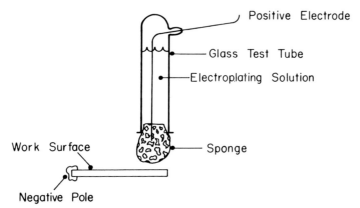

Figure 26. Hydraulic brush-plating. A readily fabricated tool

record dies, United States currency printing plates, and radar wave guides.

Seamless molds for casting polymeric artificial heart chambers have been electroformed over silvered wax cores (36) using a copper sulfate bath. Once the desired thickness is achieved, the wax is melted away leaving a smooth one piece form into which polymers can be rotation molded. Unwanted silver can be removed by wiping the surface with dilute chromic acid solution.

The following are typical formulations for electroforming baths:

Copper

Copper sulfate	30–33 oz/gal
Sulfuric acid	6–10 oz/gal

Temperature: 80–110 F
Current density: 30–150 amps/ft^2 at 6 volts

Nickel

Nickel sulfamate	40–60 oz/gal
Nickel chloride	0–2 oz/gal
Boric acid	4–6 oz/gal

Temperature: 100–140 F
pH: 3.5–4.5
Current density: 25–200 amps/ft^2

Electroforming to produce molds for high-pressure molding of plastics consists of building up a working layer of hard nickel approximately $\frac{5}{16}$ inch thick over one half of the master pattern, the other half having been embedded in wax up to its parting line. Once the first half is completed, the wax is removed, a separating agent applied to the parting line and the second half electroformed directly against the remaining half. The resulting mold is a completely accurate fit at all points, especially accurate at the parting line. The bulk of the mold is achieved by plating a $\frac{3}{4}$ inch layer of copper. These nickel-copper shells are then embedded into steel or bronze housings to withstand the high pressures of compression molding. Alternately, the mold shell can be backed by metallizing with a high temperature metal spray gun and machining to a suitable size and shape for mounting in a press.

Duplicating Materials

Duplicating materials are valuable in reproducing exact copies of body sections or simply constructing molds. An impression is obtained of the area to be copied and solidifying liquids are cast into these to form patterns. Materials most often used for duplicating are as follows:

Agar-Agar

There are two distinctly different types of hydrocolloid impression gels; those which are reversible from a hot melt state to a solid gel on cooling, such as gelatin and agar-agar, and those which progress irreversibly from a sol to a solid gel such as alginate.

Agar-agar is a linear polymer containing a sulfuric ester group and is extracted from various seaweeds. The gel changes to a sol between 207 to 225 F and reverts back to a gel at 99 F; variations from batch to batch may alter these temperatures slightly. A typical commercially available formulation (37) might consist of the following:

Agar-agar	14.3 pbw
Borax®	0.2 pbw
Potassium sulfate	2.0 pbw
Water	83.5 pbw

Most gels will change dimensions if water is allowed to escape from them by drying. To prevent this, the impression can be stored in a 2% solution of potassium sulfate or 100% relative humidity until ready to use. If plaster is to be cast into agar impressions, an accelerator such as sodium or potassium silico-fluoride should be incorporated into the plaster to reduce the inhibiting effect of the agar.

Sodium and Potassium Alginates

Alginates are salts of alginic acid which have been extracted from marine kelp. The use of aginates as impression materials involves a chemical change from a viscous sol to an irreversible gel. This transformation involves reacting the water-soluble alginate with calcium sulfate to produce the insoluble calcium alginate. Usually trisodium phosphate is included as an inhibitor to allow for convenient gelation time. The following is a typical formulation:

Potassium alginate	12 pbw
Diatomaceous earth	70 pbw
Calcium sulfate (dihydrate)	12 pbw
Trisodium phosphate	2 pbw

Best results are obtained by mixing 15 g of the above powder with 50 cc of water. Vigorous stirring for about one minute produces a smooth texture that is not tacky. Immediately place the alginate mix in or over the object to be copied and allow it to gel undisturbed for six to eight minutes at room temperature.

Rudd and co-workers (38) have pointed out the need for precise procedures when using irreversible alginate impression materials. This is especially essential when accurate reproducibility is necessary. They suggest that the alginates should be kept clean and dry and that distilled water should be used with all mixes. The temperature of the water to be added to this mix will control the setting time. Two types can be purchased, those setting in three minutes and those setting in four minutes.

Gelatin Molds

Expendable mandrels or cores of water-soluble gelatin have played a role in developing circulator assist devices (39). Conventional gelatin is poured into a metal form to give it shape; once solidified it can be smoothed or modified by rubbing against a water-wet surface.

Estane polyurethanes have been solvent-cast against the gelatin to form hollow balloon shapes once the gelatin is washed away.

Acrylamide Gel

Acrylamide gel duplicating material is made from a mixture of two organic monomers, acrylamide and N,N,'-methylene-bisacrylamide, plus a catalyst combination consisting of ammonium persulfate and B-dimethylaminopropionitrile * and water. Dootz (40) has added a filler to increase stiffness and a potassium alginate gel to minimize stickiness. When the mix is catalyzed it gels within four to five minutes. If gypsum is to be subsequently cast against the gel, the gel must first be soaked in a 2% solution of ammonium persulfate. The following is Dootz's formulation:

Acrylamide	9.5 pbw
(American Cyanamid Co.)	
N,N'-methylenebisacrylamide	0.5 pbw
Ammonium persulfate	0.6 pbw
Microcel E	5.0 pbw
(Johns Manville)	
Potassium ferrocyanide	0.0044 pbw
B-dimethylaminopropionitrite	0.5 pbw
Potassium alginate	1.0 pbw
(Kelmar Regular, Kelco Co.)	
Water	83.0 pbw

Natural Rubber Mold Materials

Rubber molds can be made from natural rubber latex, polysulfide rubber, flexible hot-melts and RTV silicone rubber.

Four methods of mold-making using natural rubber latex are possible (41). In each, a coating of latex is applied and allowed to dry; the resultant rubber layer faithfully reproduces any detail present in the master pattern.

METHOD I. Pure gum molds are made by successive dips or

* Available as Cyanogum 41 or AM-9 Chemical Grout, American Cyanamid.

repeated brushing of prevulcanized or vulcanizing dispersions of latex onto the surface of an object. Prevulcanized latex is an emulsion of fully vulcanized rubber particles and requires only drying to obtain an elastic film; vulcanizing dispersions, on the other hand, are latices of concentrated natural rubber. The latex contains a vulcanizing ingredient which requires oven curing to develop its properties.

METHOD II. This method is similar to method I except that fillers are added to the latex to impart rigidity necessary for large unsupported shapes. Wood flour, ground whiting, buca clay, cotton flock or granulated cork are added to the latex until a stiff mix results. This mix is then spread over the master pattern to the desired build-up. A preliminary coat of latex using method I reproduces greater detail.

METHOD III. The cast rubber mold is reinforced with a plaster of Paris jacket. This is usually necessary for castings of large bulk which have severe undercuts; the plaster jacket is cracked away.

METHOD IV. Hollow castings are made by filling a dry plaster of Paris mold with latex compound and allowing it to stand until the desired deposit is achieved through loss of water. Excess latex is drained from the mold and the mold is dried at 150 to 212 F until the rubber is firm. The casting is then fully vulcanized as with the other latex methods.

TABLE 38

TYPICAL LATEX RUBBER CASTING COMPOUNDS (41)

Material	Flexible	Rigid pbw	Hard
Latex, 60% conc.	167	167	167
Stabilizer, 10% casein soln.	—	5	5
Vulcanizing dispersion:			
Sulphur	1.5	3	3
Zinc oxide	1.5	5	5
ZDC *	1	1	1
Dispersing agent	0.4	0.8	0.8
Water	3.6	10.2	10.2
Filler slurry:			
Whiting	100	300	300
1% wetting agent	26	78	78
Hardener, 50% PVA emulsion	—	—	10
Vulcanize, 212 F, 30 minutes			

* Zinc dibutyldithiocarbamate
Note: Not intended for implants.

Table 38 gives typical formulations for flexible, rigid and hard latex rubber mold compounds. Commercial materials (Lotol 6982-Y, Naugatuck Chem. Co., Latex Mold Material, Industrial Products Div., B.F. Goodrich, Co., or Fry Plastics International Inc.) which are ready to use are more convenient and produce similar results.

Polysulfide Rubber Impression Material

This elastomeric impression material consists of a reactive two component system, one of which is the liquid polysulfide polymer and the other is a combination of lead peroxide (PbO_2) and sulfur. The sulfur increases the physical properties of the polysulfide while the lead peroxide acts as a polymerizing agent. The following is one composition (42) used by dentists for obtaining impressions of the mouth:

Ingredient	pbw
Paste (Part 1)	
Polysulfide polymer	79.72
Zinc oxide	4.89
Calcium sulfate	15.39
Accelerator (Part 2)	
Lead peroxide	77.65
Sulfur	3.52
Castor oil	16.84
Other	1.99

Usually these materials are packaged by the manufacturers (Permlastic, Kerr Mfg. Co., or Polytrans, Dental Perfection Co.) in squeeze tubes with orifices of predetermined size. Once an equal length of both components are extruded onto a mixing slab, they are properly proportioned.

Accelerating or inhibiting the setting time of polysulfide rubber can be accomplished with little effect on ultimate properties by regulating the amount of accelerator. As with many elastomeric impression materials, dimensional stability is best at first and diminishes with time.

Flexible Hot Melt Mold Materials

A liquid vinyl mold-making dispersion (Tam Mold, Tamite Industries, Inc.) suitable for casting epoxies, polyesters and polyurethanes is available. The single component material is heated to 350 to 400 F and poured over the master pattern in the usual manner. The mold is ready to use as soon as it cools to room temperature and is reported to reproduce fine detail. Molds which are unlimited in size can be cast; unused material can be remelted. This material can be purchased in ranges of hardness from 26 to 32 durometer Shore A (43).

Other flexible hot melt mold materials are Liqmold (Fry Plastics International Inc.), Flexmold (Fry Plastics International Inc.), EZ-Cast 521 (Aremco Products, Inc.) and Hysol AC4332 (Hysol Corp.).

Liqmold® can take the shape of molds when heated to 220 to 260 F. At this temperature it permanently solidifies into a rubber-like material.

Flexmold® is a very soft, green colored hot melt for flexible molds that can be reclaimed by reheating. The recommended melting range is 310 to 340 F.

EZ-Cast 521® plastic molding compound and Hysol AC4332® are heat fusible materials that flow readily at room temperature but harden into tough pliable, rubber-like resins at 300 F when baked for one hour.

RTV Mold-Making Silicone Rubber

The room temperature vulcanizing silicone elastomers are heavy viscosity fluids that set to a firm rubber when the appropriate catalyst is used. These materials are ideal flexible mold-making rubbers. Marcroft and co-workers (44) have shown that silicone RTV rubber (Silastic RTV 382 Dow Corning Corp.) is "an accurate mold material when used in the usual dental prosthetic laboratory conditions."

The working time is dependent on the amount and type of catalyst used. Table 39 gives typical properties of silicone mold-making rubber.

Boretos and co-workers (31) have used a low-viscosity RTV (RTV-11, General Electric Co.) with stannous octoate catalyst to obtain impressions of the brain but is not to be implanted.

Ceramic Mold Materials

Rigid molds and models can be made from gypsum and water soluble compounds of inorganic salts. Gypsum is a min-

TABLE 39

TYPICAL PROPERTIES OF SILICONE RTV
MOLD-MAKING RUBBER (45)

Property Before Catalyzing	A	B	Silastic C	D
Color	White	White	Red	Red
Flow	Pourable	Pourable	Nil	Pourable
Viscosity, poise	140	300	8,000	300
RTV to catalyst, *				
100:1 ratio:				
working time (min)	4	5	5	5
cure time (min)	20	25	15	15
200:1 ratio:				
working time (min)	10	8	10	10
cure time (hrs)	$1\frac{1}{2}$	$1\frac{1}{2}$	$\frac{1}{3}$	$\frac{1}{3}$
400:1 ratio:				
working time (min)	60	—	25	—
cure time (hrs)	$2\frac{1}{2}$	—	$\frac{3}{4}$	—
Property After Vulcanizing				
72 hours @ 77 F				
Durometer, Shore A	45	60	65	60
Tensile strength (psi)	400	600	650	600
Ultimate elongation (%)	180	120	180	100
Shrinkage (linear percent) after				
24 hours @ 77 F	0.3	0.2	0.3	0.2

* Stannous octoate.
Note: These RTVs are not to be implanted.

eral consisting of calcium sulfate dihydrate ($CaSO_4 2H_2O$). A dental stone is produced when gypsum is calcined under steam pressure at 248 to 266 F; in the presence of water, an alpha-hemihydrate is formed which is stronger than plaster or gypsum. It develops great compressive strength, however, it is readily cracked under lateral forces.

The powder should be accurately weighed and mixed with a precise amount of water to develop optimum properties. It is best sifted into the water and mixed under partial vacuum until a smooth, creamy paste is achieved. The liquid stone is gently vibrated over the model or impression, taking care to slowly fill depressions. The leading edge of the flowing stone should be kept thin and slowly moving until the model is completely covered. Gypsum will give off heat due to crystallization. Rudd (46) recommends that the fresh but firm casting be placed, for three to five minutes, in a slurry of supersaturated gypsum made by soaking old casts in water for forty-eight hours. The casting can be handled in one hour but should age one to three hours before further processing.

Water-soluble inorganic salt (Rigidax W.S., Arguesco Co., Inc., or Boil-soft, Ransom and Randolph Co.) has been used to produce dissolvable cores for molds. The material is heated until liquid by constantly stirring pellets in a beaker over a hot plate. The melt is poured into a two-part mold and rotated until a hollow shell is formed (about 15 minutes). The surface of the finished mandrel is granular in nature and must be smoothed by coating with polyvinyl alcohol solution (Elvanol 7260, E.I. du Pont de Nemours Co., Inc.) (39).

REFERENCES

1. Dupont Information Bulletin: *Lucite Acrylic Resin Embedment of Specimens.* Plastics Dept., E.I. du Pont de Nemours Co., Inc., Wilmington, Delaware.
2. Winkler, S., and McCullen, K.L.: Embedding specimens in crystal clear acrylic. *Dental Digest*, August 1964.
3. Fairchild, J.M., and Kelly, E.K.: Centrifugal casting process for resin-base dentures. *J Prosthet Dent*, 21:607–612, 1969.
4. Braunwald, N.S., Cooper, T., and Morrow, A.G.: Complete replacement of the mitral valve. *J Thorac Cardiovasc Surg*, 40:1–11, 1960.
5. Properties of encapsulating compounds. Product data. *Electronic Products Mag*, April 1963, pp. 46–55.
6. *Technical Bulletin SC:55–69*, Allyl glycidyl ether (AGE) and phenyl glycidyl ether (PGE) as reactive diluents for Epon resins, Shell Chem. Co., N.Y., 1955.
7. Bartlett, J.R.: Insulating microelectrodes by centrifuging. *Electroenceph Clin Neurophysiol*, 21:304–305, 1966.
8. Frank, N.R., and Yoder, R.E.: A method of making a flexible cast of the lung. *J Appl Physiol*, 21:1925–1926, 1965.
9. Segarra, J.M.: A new embedding procedure for the preservation of pathologic specimens using clear silicone potting compounds. *Techn Bull Regist Med Techn*, 33:191–194, 1963.
10. Lee, H., Stoffey, D.G., and Abroson, F.: Development of materials for artificial hearts and blood oxygenators. In *Artificial Heart Program Conference Proceedings* edited by R.I. Hegyeli. June 1969, Washington, D.C., Supt of Docs, USGPO, pp. 143–151.
11. Merendino, K.A.: *Prosthetic Valves for Cardiac Surgery.* Springfield, Charles C Thomas, 1961.
12. Processing Data Sheet: *Natural Rubber Latex Dipping Compounds.* The B.F. Goodrich Co., Adhesives Div, Akron, Ohio.
13. Parechanian, J.H., U.S. Rubber Co.: Personal communication.
14. Boretos, J.W.: Procedures for the fabrication of segmented poly-

urethane-polymers into useful biomedical prostheses. *National Institutes of Health, Special Publication,* 1968.

15. Boretos, J.W., Detmer, D.E., and Donachy, J.H.: Segmented polyurethane: A polyether polymer, II. Two years experience. *J Biomed Mater Res,* 5:373–387, 1971.

16. Peck, C.M., Schummacher, F.V., and Niiranen, J.V.: Resilient plastic replicas of pathologic specimens. *U.S. Armed Forces Med J,* 4:839–845, 1953.

17. Firtell, D.N., and Bartlett, S.O.: Maxillofacial prostheses: Reproducible fabrication. *J Prosthet Dent,* 22:247–252, 1969.

18. Bartlett, S.O., Pineda, L.T., and Moore, D.J.: Surface characterization of the silicone rubber prosthesis. *J Prosthet Dent,* 25:69–71, 1971.

19. Topaz, S.R.: Silastic artificial hearts constructed on wax molds. *Cleve Clin Q, 31:*49–52, 1964.

20. Kessler, T.R., Foote, J.L., Andrade, J.D., and Kolff, W.J.: Methods to construct artificial organs. *Trans Am Soc Artif Intern Organs,* 17:36–40, 1971.

21. Purkis, F.T.: Latex applications. *India-Rubber J,* Jan. 1938, pp. 13–19.

22. Ghosh, J.C.: Rubber latex composition. *Indian Rubber,* 32:970, 1947.

23. Kosse, A.J.: Written communication.

24. Boucher, L.J.: Injected silastic for tissue protection. *J Prosth Dent,* 15:73–82, 1965.

25. Mandarino, M.P., and Salvatore, J.E.: Polyurethane polymer: Its use in fractured and diseased bone. *Am J Surg,* 97:442–446, 1959.

26. Niiranen, J.V.: The Navy's plastic ocular restoration. *The Military Surgeon, 100:*5, 1947.

27. Sheldon, C.H., Pudenz, R.H., Restarski, S.S., and Craig, W.M.: The lucite calvarium—A method for direct observation of the brain. *J Neurosurg., 1:*67–75, 1944.

28. Braunwald, N.S., Morrow, A.G., DeBroske, J.M.F., Hamilton, W.D., and Boretos, J.W.: Accelerated fatigue testing of available pacemaker electrodes and Elgiloy wire coils. *Surgery,* 58:846–850, 1965.

29. Carow, G.E.: Crosslinkable polyethylene improves rotomolded products. *Plastics Design and Processing, 11:*18–20, 1971.

30. Gaertner, R.A.: A new Teflon intravascular catheter. *Surg Gynecol Obstet,* Sept. 1964, pp. 599–600.

31. Boretos, J.W., Bourke, R.S., Nelson, K.M., Naumann, R.A., and Ommaya, A.K.: Technique for unilateral isolation of the subdural space in the intact primate. *J Neurosurg., 35:*101–107, 1971.

32. Ore, S., Sebestyen, J.G., and Stone, W., Jr.: Preparation of surgical implants from silicone rubber by means of a postforming technique. *Surgery,* 52:385–390, 1962.

33. Barsoum, W.M., and El-Ebrashi, M.K.: The construction of individ-

ualized plastic teeth from beryllium-copper molds. *J Prosthet Dent,* 17:251–259, 1967.

34. Meltable mandrel proves vital in molding artificial heart. *Product Engineering,* Aug. 1, 1966.

35. *Dow Corning Bulletin 08–104.* Electroforming applications using Silastic RTV flexible mold making materials. Dow Corning Corp, Midland, Michigan.

36. McCabe, S.M., Personal communication.

37. Preble, B.: *Dental Impression Compositions.* U.S. Patent 2,234,383 (March 11, 1941).

38. Rudd, K.D., Morrow, R.M., and Strunk, R.R.: Accurate alginate impressions. *J Prosthet Dent,* 22:294–300, 1969.

39. Sprung, J.: Development of fabrication technology for circulatory assist devices. In *Artificial Heart Program Conference, Proceedings, June 9–13, 1969,* edited by R.J. Hegyeli. Washington, D.C. Supt of Doc, USGPO, pp. 679–688.

40. Dootz, E.R., Craig, R.G., and Peyton, F.A.: Aqueous acrylamide gel duplicating material. *J Prosthet Dent,* 17:570–577, 1967.

41. *Natural Rubber Technical Information Sheets 88 and 49.* The Natural Rubber Producers Research Assoc, Hertz, England.

42. Pearson, S.L.: A new elastic impression material: A preliminary report. *Brit Dent J,* 99:72–76, 1955.

43. Plastics Design and Processing: *Flexible Mold Material for Casting.* Nov. 20, 1971.

44. Marcroft, K.R., Tencate, R.L., and Skinner, E.W.: The effects of heat, aging, and mold separation on the dimensional stability of silicone rubber. *J Prosthet Dent,* 14:1091–1098, 1964.

45. Bulletin 61–008a: *Information About Mold-Making Materials.* Dow Corning Corp, Midland, Michigan, June, 1970.

46. Rudd, K.D., Morrow, R.M., and Bange, A.A.: Accurate casts. *J Prosthet Dent,* 21:545–554, 1969.

V

GUTTMANN (1) describes the phenomenon of adhesion as either mechanical or chemical in nature. Those bonds achieved through mechanical means constitute a glue line that physically interlocks both surfaces; whereas chemical bonds consist of an attraction of molecular forces between the surfaces to be bonded and the adhesive. These molecular forces could be the result of unsatisfied primary and secondary valence structure, electrical attraction such as van der Waal's forces, or dipoles and may act singly or in combination. Sharpe (2) and co-workers, however, feel that adhesives stick primarily as a result of being close together. They have demonstrated the importance of low surface-free energy for completely wetting the surface by the adhesive. Regardless of the theory involved, we are aware that specific materials and technics are necessary to achieve the best possible bonds.

Adhesive cements can be conveniently classed into three categories: solvent, dope and chemical. Manufacturers of cements are many and produce numerous varieties for both general and special purposes. The recommendations given here, therefore, serve only as a general guide.

Solvent cements are chosen on the basis of their ability to dissolve a polymer, their evaporation rate and the convenience and safety of handling. When using this type of cement for joining two similar materials, an appropriate amount is applied to the joints which are held under pressure until all solvent is evaporated, the joint interface stabilized and an integral bond formed. More than one solvent is applicable for most plastics, and often the choice of cement is less critical than the way it is used. An excessive amount, combined with a tight fit, can result in serious stress failures.

Dope cements are used when the loose fit of a part must be corrected during the joining operation. This method is similar to solvent cementing, except that the cement consists of a thick syrup of material made by dissolving chips of the base material in an appropriate solvent. Any solvent which can dissolve a given polymer can be used to make a dope cement for that substance. Evaporation time is often an important consideration.

Chemical cements are composed of a resin and a cross-linking agent. No solvent is present, and solidification begins after the two components are mixed. Depending on the type of resin, its cross-linking agent and other additives, adhesives with varying physical properties from soft and flexible to hard and rigid can be tailored. Roughen and thoroughly wash and dry the surface of the plastic or rubber prior to bonding. This provides an enlarged and somewhat undercut area for the adhesive, as well as a clean surface free from oxides, fingerprints, oils and other contaminants which could interfere with the ultimate bond. Dissimilar materials in contact often produce adverse migration of their chemical components and rarely should be joined by any bonding method other than chemical cementing. An intermediate adhesive, compatible with both, is required.

For some cement joints, up to seven or more days are required to develop maximum strength and therefore prototypes should be tested before actual use.

BONDING PLASTICS

Many varieties of materials are used in the biomedical materials laboratory in conjunction with auxillary apparatus used for implant devices; these materials serve as indispensable tools in the hands of the engineer. Proper use of cement to join these plastics together is essential. Table 40 lists many of these and suggests applicable means of bonding them together.

TABLE 40

AN ADHESIVE REFERENCE GUIDE FOR PLASTICS

(Methods and cements vary with type of plastic)

Material (Ref. No.)	Solvent Cement	Dope Cement	Chemical Cement
ABS (3)	Methyl ethyl ketone	Resin & solvent	Epoxy adhesive
Acetal (4)	(Not applicable)	(Not applicable)	Oxidation treatment and "Cycleweld" C-14
Acrylic (5)	Methylene chloride or ethylene dichloride	Resin & solvent	PS-18, PS-30, or East-man 910
Cellophane, un-coated (6)	(Not applicable)	(Not applicable)	Epoxy
Kel-F (7, 8)	(Not applicable)	(Not applicable)	Sodium etch and epoxy or silicone RTV adhesive
Mylar (9)	(Not applicable)	(Not applicable)	Polyester
Nylon (10)	12% Aqueous phenol	(Not applicable)	"Penacolite" G1124, Eastman 910, or "Cycle-weld" C-6
Phenylene oxide (11)	Ethylene dichloride + 5% Carbon tetra-chloride	(Not applicable)	Oxidation treatment & rubber-base, epoxy or silicone RTV adhesive
Polycarbonate (12)	Methylene chloride or ethylene dichloride	Resin & solvent	Epoxy with diethylene triamine hardener, sili-cone RTV adhesive, or Eastman 910
Polyethylene (13)	(Not applicable)	(Not applicable)	Oxidation treatment and flexible epoxy or polysul-fide adhesive
Polypropylene (13)	(Not applicable)	(Not applicable)	Oxidation treatment and flexible epoxy or polysul-fide adhesive
Polystyrene (14)	Xylene	Resin & solvent	Rubber-base or epoxy adhesive
Polyurethane	Tetrahydrofuran or dimethylacetamide	Resin & solvent	Epoxy adhesive
Teflon, FEP, TFE, (7, 15)	(Not applicable)	(Not applicable)	Sodium etch and epoxy or silicone RTV adhesive
Thermosetting plastics (16)	(Not applicable)	(Not applicable)	Epoxy adhesive or sili-cone RTV adhesive
Vinyls (rigid & flexible)	Tetrahydrofuran	Resin & solvent	Epoxy adhesive (for rigid vinyl only)

Note: Not intended for implants.

Alkyl 2-Cyanoacrylate

Fast-acting adhesives such as the alkyl 2-cyanoacrylates [*], used for bonding almost all types of plastic, metal and rubber (except silicone) are popular. Coover (17) suggests that the most important factors affecting the bonding action and the

[*] Eastman 910, Eastman Chemical Products, Inc.

setting times of this adhesive are the types of materials being bonded and the condition of the bonding surface. Bonds involving smooth, hard surfaces set more rapidly than those between porous or rough surfaces. An alkaline surface such as glass will form unbreakable bonds within ten to thirty seconds but on the other hand, slightly acid surfaces such as wood require three or more minutes to set.

Homologs of cyanoacrylate have been investigated for anastomoses of tissue and have enjoyed various degrees of success (18). The material is biodegradable and the methyl homolog is lethal to laboratory animals (19). The butyl homolog, when mixed with calcium hemihydrate, is comparable in toxicity in the mouth to zinc oxide and eugenol paste (20).

Gelatin Resorcinol

Tatooles and Braunwald (21) used a gelatin resorcinol adhesive cross-linked with formaldehyde as a hemostatic agent to control bleeding from the liver and kidney. Koehnlein and Lemperle (22) further investigated the use of gelatin-resorcinol-formaldehyde glue and concluded that it possessed the following advantages over acrylic glues: "(a) good applicability to bleeding surfaces, (b) minimal histotoxicity . . . . (c) minimal heat development during condensation, (d) lasting elasticity with no calcification, (e) relatively fast phagocytosis without giant cells or inflammatory reaction, (f) higher viscosity and slower binding than acrylic glues, therefore technically easier application, (g) no diminished wound healing, wound separation, or infection in 212 tests; no complications."

Epoxy for Cellophane

It is interesting to note that some bonded thin plastic films show good tensile properties but exhibit poor strength under a stripping action, whereas others are extremely difficult to bond under the best circumstances. Markley and Robinette (6) have developed an adhesive for dialysis casing made from cellophane by utilizing an epoxy-cellulose covalent bond concept. The bond is made using diglycidyl ether of bisphenol A (DER 332, Dow Chemical Co., or Epon 828, Shell Chemical Co.) and either of five aliphatic amine curing agents. In each case 40 percent of the epoxy groups were left unreacted by using only 60 percent of the stoichiometric amounts for the amines. Three of these are diethylenetriamine, for example, 5 to 8 phr; triethylenetetramine, for example, 7 to 9 phr; tetraethylenepentamine, for example, 7 to 8 phr. Each adhesive formulation was cured at 150 F to produce the bond. (*See* epoxy resins, Ch. I.)

Polyethylene Bonding Systems

High-density polyethylene * and others can be successfully bonded using special procedures which will allow the wax-like, nonpolar surface to be fully "wetted." Surface wetting is necessary to obtain a good bond. Devine and co-workers (23) have described six ways to achieve a receptive surface on polyethylene: flame treatment, sanding, acid treatment plus oven drying at 154 F and 194 F, acid treatment plus wiping and air drying at 72 F, and acid treatment and acetone drying.

The treatments:

1. *Flame treatment* consists of passing the specimen quickly through the oxidizing flame of a Bunsen burner until all gloss is removed from the surface.
2. *Sanding* consists of sanding away the old glossy surface with 400-A aluminum oxide abrasive paper.
3. *Acid treatment* is accomplished by immersing into the following at 140 F for five minutes:

Potassium dichromate	75 pbw
Water	120 pbw
Conc. sulfuric acid	1,500 pbw

The polyethylene is rinsed in tap water following one of the above treatments and dried by one of the following methods:

4. Acetone dry
5. Wipe with a clean cloth and air dry
6. Oven dry at 154 F
7. Oven dry at 194 F

---

* Marlex 6002, Phillips Petroleum Company.

Immediately after each treatment, one of the following adhesives were applied and cured seventy-two hours at 74 F; postcured, four hours at 120 F; and conditioned at 74 F, 50 percent R.H. for twenty-four hours:

An Epoxy Adhesive

Epon 820	7 pbw
(Shell Chemical Company)	
Versamid 140	3 pbw
(General Mills, Inc.)	
Cab-o-sil filler	½ pbw
(Cabot Chemical Company)	

A Polyester Adhesive

Laminac 4116	90 pbw
(American Cyanamid Corp.)	
Laminac 4134	10 pbw
Cab-o-sil	4 pbw
Methyl ethyl ketone peroxide	1.6 pbw
(60% solution)	

A Nitrile-Rubber-Phenolic Adhesive

Pliobond 30	use as received
(Goodyear Tire & Rubber Co.)	

Table 41 gives typical values for bond strengths of these adhesives and surface treatments for polyethylene. Polysulfide rubber has been similarly used as an adhesive following this treat-

TABLE 41

BOND STRENGTH OF POLYETHYLENE USING THREE ADHESIVES
AND SIX SURFACE TREATMENTS (23)

	Average Shear Strength of Adhesives, psi *		
Treatment	Epoxy	Polyester	Nitrite-Rubber-Phenolic
Control	46	85	44
Flame treated	480 †	434 †	138
Sanded	195	175	56
Acid, plus oven dried 154 F	457 †	297	108
Acid, oven dried 194 F	475 †	277	96
Acid, wiped, air dried 72 F	499 †	357 †	110
Acid, acetone dried	497 †	394 †	112

* Average of 5 tests.
† Polyethylene failed rather than bond.
Note: Not intended for implants.

ment. Commercially available etchants * to promote adhesion to polyolifins are available and work reasonably well.

Teflon Bonding System

To bond Teflon special surface preparation is necessary. Nelson and co-workers (7) report the use of a sodium/naphthalene/tetrahydrofuran bath to chemically etch the surface of Teflon, thus rendering it suitable to adhesion. The technic consists of immersing the part for several seconds in the following:

Sodium metal †	23 g
Napthalene	128 g
Tetrahydrofuran	1 liter
Stir 2 hours @ R.T.	

The part is removed from the bath, rinsed and dried well. The carbonaceous film, thus achieved, provides bond strength capability greater than the Teflon itself when a suitable adhesive is applied; the epoxies work well. Commercial preparations, ready for use, are available.‡

BONDING RUBBER

Medical devices made of multiple elastomeric components often require joining by means of an adhesive. Where rubber-to-rubber bonds are required or where dissimilar materials are to be joined, rubber adhesives are invaluable, especially for flexibility at the interface. Each set of conditions requires special consideration; for medical implants only nontoxic and sterile materials can be used. Table 42 lists typical industrial rubber adhesives according to the base elastomer from which they are made. Most of these are general purpose adhesives while others bond only elastomers which consist of the same base. Although these are not medically acceptable, they do offer suggested materials for assembling auxillary medical equipment.

In the raw state most rubber will adhere to itself and become permanently attached as long as tight contact is maintained dur-

---

* Poly-Prep, Chemclean Products Corp.
† Use extreme caution as sodium metal is highly unstable.
‡ Tetra-Etch, W.L. Gore & Associates, or Gem-Bond Epoxy Bonding Agent, Applied Plastics.

TABLE 42

TYPICAL INDUSTRIAL
RUBBER ADHESIVES *

Butadiene-acrylonitrile copolymer
    (buna N or nitrile rubber)
Butadiene-styrene copolymer
    (SBR, formerly GR-S)
Butyl rubber
Carboxylic elastomers
Chlorinated rubber
Cyclized rubber
    by sulfuric acid
    by stannic chloride
Isocyanate rubber
Natural rubber
Phenolic resins blended with
    buna N
    neoprene
    neoprene-nylon
Polychloroprene (neoprene)
Polysulfide rubber
Reclaim rubber
Rubber hydrochloride
Silicone rubber

* Taken in part from Ref. 24.
Note: Not intended for implants.

ing vulcanization. Quite often, however, the use of primers is necessary to promote adhesion or to maintain it under environmental conditions.

NATURAL RUBBER

Good bonds with natural rubber and metal are achieved by first brass plating the metal (25). Rubber surfaces which are fully vulcanized can be joined by the use of a solvent cement such as Vulcalock (B.F. Goodrich Co.) or for bonding dissimilar material a tie-gum can be used (26). Attaching inflatable rubber balloons to the ends of polyvinyl chloride catheters, for instance, requires a very special cement (27). Bond strengths to vinyl of over 100 psi at 212 F are possible using a solution of natural rubber and methyl methacrylate graft polymer. Table 43 lists a typical formulation for making the adhesive in quantities of less than ½ gallon. Temperature rise in the polymer must be kept below 105 F.

Mix all of Group A together and slowly add to this all of Group B. Allow the mixture to stand for thirty minutes so that good absorption of the monomer into the rubber particles occurs.

TABLE 43

NATURAL RUBBER TO POLYVINYL CHLORIDE
ADHESIVE SYSTEM (27)

Group A	*Wet Weight (gm)*
Natural latex	100
(60% dry content)	
Dispersol LN (20% solution)	3
(Disodium salt of methylene	
dinaphthalene sulphonic acid.)	
Ammonia (2% solution)	56.5
Group B	
Methyl methacrylate monomer	42
(not to contain more than 0.01%	
hydroquinone inhibitor)	
Tert-butyl hydroperoxide	0.21
Oleic acid	0.3
Group C	
Tetra-ethylene pentamine	1.95
(10% solution)	

The TEP from Group C is added slowly, with constant stirring, and allowed to set for one hour. The polyvinyl chloride surface is cleaned of any exuded plasticizer and a thin layer of the adhesive is applied and allowed to dry. The uncured rubber for the balloon is placed against the bond area, under pressure, and then heat cured.

POLYURETHANE

Polyurethanes can be made to bond to themselves by the use of solvent dopes. The elastomer is dissolved in such solvents as tetrahydrofuran or dimethylacetamide to a solid content of up to 30 percent. By using various adhesives and special surface preparation, bonding to metal can be achieved. Table 44 shows typical bond strengths achieved with segmented polyurethane [*] and stainless steel. Special primers can also help with other polyurethanes (28).

SILICONE RUBBER

Convenient and ready-to-use silicone adhesives can be used to develop strong bonds between silicone elastomers, metal, polymethyl methacrylate, Dacron and etched Teflon, (see *Teflon*, Ch. V). These adhesives cure at room temperature on exposure to air moisture and on the release of acetic acid. One

---

[*] Biomer, Ethicon Corp.

TABLE 44

ADHESION OF SEGMENTED POLYURETHANE TO
VARIOUS SURFACES

Substrate	Surface Finish	Adhesive System	Mean Adhesive Strength *
Stainless steel	Polished	Direct	5.6
Stainless steel	Brushed	Direct	7.0
Stainless steel	Sand blasted	Direct	9.6
Stainless steel	Brushed	Epoxy EA-40 (1 to 1) †	6.1
Stainless steel	Brushed	Epoxy EA-40 (2 to 1)	8.1
Stainless steel	Brushed	Chemlock 607 ‡	23.6
Stainless steel	Brushed	Primer A-29550 §	23.4
Stainless steel	Brushed	Chem-grip epoxy ‖	7.4
Teflon	Brushed	Chem-grip epoxy	6.2

* Strength @ lb/in—Tests consisted of 3 specimens each.
† Smooth-on Mfg. Co.
‡ Lord Mfg. Co.
§ Bradley and Vroohman Co.
‖ Chemplast Inc.

brand * has been carefully prepared for use in medical applications and can be used in the raw state against living tissues with very little problems.

The following are the surface preparations to be used with this type of silicone adhesive:

1. Thoroughly clean with acetone and non-oily soap in hot water to remove surface contamination.
2. Rinse copiously.
3. Apply an adhesive layer 0.020″ to 0.030″ thick, never less than 0.005″.
4. Allow to cure twenty-four hours—several days for optimum bond strength.

Other adhesives and primers which give good results in promoting adhesion between raw or vulcanized silicone rubber are available (29). Of particular value are Dow Corning 796 Primer (Dow Corning Corp.) and Chemlock 607 Primer (Hughson Chemical Co.). These latter two materials are widely used for priming Dacron cloth prior to impregnating with medical silicone rubber and although they are believed to be inert, no toxicological data is available.

We have repeatedly emphasized the importance of avoiding frictional heat build-up on plastic surfaces because of the re-

* Silastic Medical Adhesive Silicone Type A., Dow Corning Corp.

sulting softening. There are, however, conditions under which frictional surface heat can be used to advantage; for example, sealing, spin welding and hot gas welding.

SEALING

Sealing of plastic films is based on the principle of localized heating of two materials in contact to cause melting and fusing. The most common methods employed are electric impulse, dielectric and ultrasonic sealing (30); applicable to thermoplastics only.

Electric impulse apparatus for films consists of a resistance wire with a timer to control the current through the wire. The films are clamped between jaws; the switch is activated to generate heat throughout the wire; immediate melting, followed by cooling, accomplishes the fusion bond. The method is limited to simple tool designs, thin films and readily softened plastics.

Dielectric sealing uses a radio frequency generating apparatus with an electrode die and a ground plate. Power is adjustable for whatever plastic film thickness is being used. Elaborate, three-dimensional seals can be made with the use of simple dies. To seal thermoplastics of high dielectric strength, the radio frequency power is augmented with heated dies and buffer sheets. Complex shapes, in three dimensions, can be made in this fashion. Figure 27 shows a polyvinyl chloride blood bag being sealed with dielectric energy.

Ultrasonic sealing results from the heating of contacting plastic surfaces, at a molecular level, by means of sound waves which agitate the polymer to a localized molten state. This method is effective for films such as polyethylene, polypropylene, fluorinated hydrocarbons, polycarbonates and many others. Standard ultrasonic equipment consists of a power source, a transducer assembly that changes the electrical energy to mechanical energy at the same frequency, and a resonant section which transmits the mechanical vibrations to the plastic interface. Although a properly tuned resonant section (known as a "horn") is necessary, effective sealing depends upon high moduli of elasticity and low melting temperatures of the plastic,

Figure 27. Radio frequency sealing. A polyvinyl chloride blood bag being sealed. Simple dies can attach tubing or complex shapes in three dimensions.

plus the proper combination of time, pressure, energy output and joint design.

Spin Welding

The process known as spin welding can often be used effectively for fastening most thermoplastics. The friction of two parts in motion against each other heat-fuses them and produces strong, permanent, leak-free joints. It is important, however, that the speed, pressure and spinning time be carefully controlled. Align the two pieces to be welded with progressive contact from the center area to the lip of the joint to prevent air entrapment and provide sufficient rigidity to prevent bulging. Rotate the parts at 1200 fpm (do not exceed 5000 fpm) and press together under approximately 200 psi. (Polypropylene and polyethylene can be spin welded at 50 to 100 psi.) Spin the parts until melting occurs at the joint; stop suddenly and maintain pressure until the weld solidifies.

Hot Gas Welding

This specialized technique of joining plastic requires a practiced operator. A special welding apparatus is used which consists of a hot gas torch, pressure regulator and a filler rod holder (31). Nitrogen gas passes through the torch and is heated to melt both the plastic joint and the filler rod. The experience of the operator and the temperature of the gas determine the speed at which joints are welded. Applicable temperatures vary according to the plastic being welded. (*See* melting temperatures of various polymers,* ch. VI.) Results are good and can produce joints 90 percent as strong as the original material.

REFERENCES

1. Guttmann, W. H.: *Concise Guide to Structural Adhesives.* New York, Reinhold Publishing Company, 1961.
2. Sharpe, L.H., Schonhorn, H., and Lynch, C.J.: *Adhesives.* International Science and Technology, April 1964, pp. 26–37.
3. Machining of Cycolac Brand ABS: *Borg-Warner Technical Bulletin PB-128.* Marbon Division, Borg-Warner, Washington, W. Va.
4. *Delrin Acetal Resin Post Molding Operations Bulletin,* 1963. E.I. du Pont de Nemours & Company, Inc., Wilmington, Delaware.
5. *Rohm & Hass Plexiglas Design and Fabrication Data.* Philadelphia, Rohm & Haas, 1949.
6. Markely, F.W., and Robinette, C.J.: Developing adhesives for hemodialysis membranes. Written communication.
7. Nelson, E.R., Kilduff, T.J., and Benderly, A.A.: Bonding of Teflon. *Ind Eng Chem 50:329,* 1958.

* *Note:* Elastomers such as silicone rubber, once vulcanized, cannot be melted with heat or dissolved with any solvent. (*See* footnote on compounding, Ch. II.)

8. *Kel-F 81 Brand Plastic, Technical Information Sheet, Finishing-1.* 1961, Minnesota Mining and Manufacturing Co., St. Paul, Minn.

9. *Dupont Adhesives for Dupont Mylar Polyester Film.* Bulletin 17, E.I. du Pont de Nemours and Co., Inc., Wilmington, Delaware.

10. *Zytel Nylon Resin Machining.* Du Pont Information Bulletin No. X-47d. E.I. du Pont de Nemours Co., Inc., Wilmington, Dela.

11. *Noryl Thermoplastic Resin Bulletin.* Polymer Products Operation, General Electric Co., Pittsfield, Mass.

12. *Lexan Polycarbonate Resins.* Fabrication Data Sheet # B 11 ff and C-10, Chemical Materials Department, General Electric Co., Pittsfield, Mass.

13. Ziccarelli, J.J.: Polyolefin surface treatment methods. *Modern Plastics.* November 1962, p. 126.

14. *Dow Styron Bulletin: Machining and Mechanical Finishing.* The Dow Chemical Co., Midland, Michigan.

15. *Journal of Teflon®.* Reprint No. 11, E.I. du Pont de Nemours & Co., Inc., Wilmington, Delaware.

16. Katz, I.: *Adhesive Materials. Their Properties and Usage.* Long Beach (Calif.), Foster Publishing Co., 1964.

17. Coover, H.W., Jr.: Cyano-acrylate adhesives. *Handbook of Adhesives.* New York, Reinhold Publishing Company, 1962.

18. Page, R.C.: Tissue adhesive eliminates sutures and staples in many types of surgery. *Adhesive Age,* Dec. 1966, pp. 27–30.

19. Lewers, D.T., Just-Viera, J.O., and Yeager, G. H.: Lethal properties of a rapidly polymerizing adhesive. *Arch Surg,* 87:627–631, 1963.

20. Bhaskar, S.N., Frisch, J., and Margetis, P.M.: Tissue response to dental cement containing butyl cyanoacrylate. *J Dent Res, 48*:57–60, 1969.

21. Tatooles, C.J., and Braunwald, N.S.: The use of crosslinked gelatin as a tissue adhesive to control hemorrhage from liver and kidney. *Surgery, 60*:857–861, 1966.

22. Koehnlein, H.E., and Lemperle, G.: Experimental studies with a new gelatin-resorcin-formaldehyde. *Surgery, 66*:377–382, 1969.

23. Devine, A., Bodnar, W., Duda, E., and Bodnar, M.: Effects of surface treatments on bonding to polyethylene with various type adhesives. *Document No. AD660–276,* Clearinghouse for Federal Scientific and Technical Information, Springfield, Virginia, 22151.

24. Wetzel, F.H.: Introduction to rubber-based adhesives. In *Handbook of Adhesives,* edited by I. Skeist. New York, Reinhold Publishing Company, 1962.

25. Technical Information Sheet 105, *Natural Rubber.* The Natural Rubber Producer's Research Associations, Herts, England.

26. Booklet No. 23A, *Braze Bonding Agent, Cover Cements, A Guide to Their Effective Use in Obtaining Elastomer-to-Metal Adhesion.* R.T. Vanderbilt Co., New York, N.Y., November, 1964.

27. *Natural Rubber Technical Information Sheet 31.* The Natural Rubber Producers Research Association, Herts, England.
28. NASA Tech Brief 69–10540, *Improved Primer for Bonding Polyurethane Adhesives to Metals.* Clearinghouse for Federal Scientific and Technical Information, Springfield, Virginia, October, 1969.
29. Bulletin 02–014, *Information About Silicone Primers and Adhesives from Dow Corning.* Dow Corning, Midland, Michigan, August, 1964.
30. Farkas, R.D.: *Heat Sealing.* New York, Rheinhold Publishing Company, 1964.
31. Haim, G., and Zade, H.P.: *Welding of Plastics.* London, Crosby Lockwood, 1947.

VI

Machining of Plastics

THE DESIGN of a biomedical device from plastic is determined in great measure by the method of fabrication elected. In some cases, molding offers advantages over machining. However, machining is best employed when quantities are small, time is limited, design changes are likely, tolerances are closer than ±0.003 inch/inch and ±0.001 inch for each additional inch in length or diameter and when the plastic is difficult to mold to close tolerances. Whatever the method of fabrication, always avoid having thin walls adjacent to thick sections as these usually result in concentrated stress. Also avoid sharp corners, which provide natural points for cracks to develop. Proper design provides for

Generous fillets and rounds.

Reinforcement ribs or struts at weak areas.

Holes located remote from edges.

No thin sections of plastic around inserts.

Holes with ratio of length to diameter of at least 2½ to 1.

No sharp entering corners on holes that are to be tapped (a small countersink prevents chipping at the edge when tap is withdrawn).

Absence of outside threads on a boss extending to the face of the part. (The sharp edge produced where the thread starts away from the face will almost certainly generate a crack.)

TOOLS AND THEIR USE

Standard metal and woodworking machinery can be used for plastic machining. Kobayashi (1) has shown machinability of plastics to be dependent upon cutting forces, amount of tool wear, surface roughness, the type of material and the particular cutting operation employed. To produce effective results, therefore, careful selection of tools and attention to the following guidelines are necessary:

1. Tools are rated according to their ability to maintain sharpness at the cutting tool surface. In descending order of durability are diamond-tipped, sintered carbides, chrome-plated carbon steel and "high-speed" steel.
2. Drilling is best done with bits having a slow twist, polished flutes and a thin web. Conventional high-speed drills are usually adequate for most unreinforced plastics.
3. For thermosetting plastics, grind the cutter as for brass and adjust the rake angle to scrape, not to cut.
4. For thermoplastics, grind the cutter to peel, or shear, or both. Usually a very sharp edge is required.
5. By use of appropriate techniques it is possible to achieve tolerances of 0.001 inch or better.
6. Do not force the tool against the plastic while drilling, grinding, buffing or sanding. Light pressure produces less frictional heat and minimizes distortion.
7. Use a twist drill having a point angle of 40 to 60 degrees to prevent shattering of the underside as the drill breaks through, especially when drilling thin sections.
8. Keep all tools sharp. Dull tools can promote inaccuracy, additional stresses and possible distortion.
9. Dissipate heat as rapidly as possible from the work piece. A light solution of detergent and water prevents overheating during machining operations, although a mixture of water and air, water or air alone is often sufficient. Most cutting oils contain ingredients, such as aromatic hydrocarbons or chlorinated solvents, which attack the readily solvated polycarbonates, polystyrenes or acrylics, and are, therefore, not recommended. Porous plastics can absorb these materials and influence implant performance through undesirable tissue reactions.

Sufficient time and care must be allowed to produce the

part, otherwise quality and performance suffer and failure of a "live-saving" device could result.

Thermal properties of plastic, for example, specific heat, thermal conductivity and coefficient of expansion, play a significant role in dimensional stability. The specific heat per unit volume of plastic is smaller than that of metal. The temperature rise in the plastic part, for a given quantity of heat, is therefore larger than that in the metal tool generating the heat. The thermal conductivity of the part is generally much less than that of the metal tool which conducts most of the heat away from the plastic. The heat in the plastic, however, remains near the surface as a threat to melting and stress induction. Also, thermal expansion can seriously affect the dimensional stability when frictional heat is generated during drilling, or similar operations, which may expand the plastic. Teflon, for example, has a coefficient of thermal expansion ten times greater than that of stainless steel.

Few, if any, materials are stress-relieved by the manufacturer before shipment. An important first step, therefore, although time consuming, is to anneal (*see* annealing, Ch. VI) the plastic stock to relieve gross stresses induced during polymerization at the factory. Next, the instrument maker should machine the part to its approximate dimensions and again anneal it. The subsequent final machining operation is employed to bring the part within tolerances. All plastic parts should reach room temperature before dimensions are checked. This is particularly true for high heat distortion materials such as the fluorocarbons and the more heat-sensitive polystyrene and polyolefins.

Any plastic device used in a living system, or other high humidity environment, should be moisture-conditioned before final dimensions are measured. This is done by soaking or heating the part in water (depending on its temperature sensitivity) for several hours. Initial moisture absorption tends to remain near the surface; saturation or equilibrium may require days or months, depending on the thickness and hygroscopic nature of the plastic.

To machine a large piece from thick sections, work symmetrically, starting from the geometric center of the original piece. This minimizes warping tendencies caused by unbalanced stress set up in the material during manufacture.

Drilling

To obtain the best drilling results, a drill must be shaped to eject chips which tend to stick and pack in the flutes (Fig. 28), otherwise friction can cause surface melting. Coolants, especially air and air water mists, not only keep surface temperatures in check but assist in cleaning chips from the hole being drilled, as does frequent withdrawal of the drill bit. Speeds should be as rapid as possible, without melting the plastic; the rate of feed should be slow and even. Select optimum point and rake angles as outlined in Table 45 to minimize cracking and crazing caused

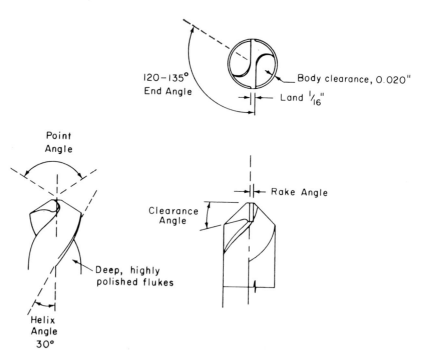

Figure 28. Drill showing important angles. (*See* Table 46 for further recommendations.)

TABLE 45

SPECIFIC RECOMMENDATIONS FOR HIGH SPEED DRILLS

Material (Refs.)	Angles in Degrees			Drill Dia. (in)	Cutting Speeds	
	Point	Rake	Clearance		rpm	*fpm
ABS (2)	90			½	150	60 to 180
Acetal (3)	118			¼	2000	
Acrylic (4)	60	0	12 to 15	⅜	1000	
Kel-F: (5)						
thin sheets	60 to 70		14 to 18	¼	400	
deep holes	100		14 to 18	½	325	
Nylon (6)	118		10 to 15	¼	800	
Phenylene oxide (7)	118	5	15	½	300	200
Polycarbonate (8, 9)	60 to 90	0 to −5	9 to 15	¼	3000	
Polyethylene (10)	70 to 90	0	12 to 18	½	1000	
Polypropylene (11)	70	0		¼	1700	
Polystyrene: (12)						
small holes	60 to 90	0 to −5	12	½	1000	
large holes	90 to 120	0 to −5	12			200 to 500
Teflon, FEP, TFE (10, 13)		0 to 15		¼	1700	
Thermosetting plastics (14)	70 to 90			½	600	

* *Note:* Formula for converting fpm to rpm: $N = \frac{4C}{D}$ where N = rpm, C = cutting speed in fpm, D = diameter of rotating part in inches.

by overheating and to safeguard against breakthrough damage. Chipping around holes drilled in acrylic and polystyrene can be minimized by reducing the applied pressure just prior to breakthrough.

Reaming

Expansion-type collar or hand reamers should be used with most thermoplastics to prevent undersized holes in resilient material that often occur when fixed reamers are used. Cutting speeds for reaming should be approximately two-thirds of those used for drilling (calculations can be made from Table 46). Helically fluted reamers are more versatile than straight-fluted ones, since they can be used on both through holes and blind holes for a smooth cut and fine finish. Boring is more accurate and convenient than reaming if the part can be lathe-turned (*see* turning, Ch. VI).

Threading and Tapping

Conventional equipment is satisfactory for threading and tapping. Avoid sharp V-threads, in or on plastic, which can break at their apex, in favor of course-pitch threads which are stronger. Make successive cuts of 0.005 inch to 0.010 inch with conventional single-pointed tools until the finished thread is produced. Tapping is best done with a three-fluted tap having rounded thread bottoms for chip clearance and a zero rake angle to prevent digging. A tap functions best when a starting hole is drilled large enough to permit only 75 percent of the full finished thread.

Turning

The cutting torque for plastics is much less than that required for most metals. General turning and boring tools are similar to those used for brass. Because of the flexibility of plastic, proper clamping and supporting fixtures are necessary to prevent chatter, loss of tolerance, rough finish and dull cutting edges. Improvised holders of rubber, tape, etcetera, can be used if tightly secured. Figure 29 depicts a typical general purpose tool.

TABLE 46

RECOMMENDATIONS FOR USE OF GENERAL PURPOSE TURNING TOOLS IN CUTTING PLASTIC *

| Material (Ref.) | a | b | c | d | Angles in Degrees | | | | Optimum Cutting Speed |
					e	f	g	h	
ABS (2, 11)	0–5	10–15			0–15	10–15	$1/16$–$3/16$	2 degrees above centerline	200–250 fpm
Acrylics (4)	0		3–5						500 rpm
Kel-F (5)	0–5	10–20			0–5	5–10	$1/32$		980 rpm @ 610 fpm
Nylon (6)	0–5	20	45	45	0	15–20	0		550 rpm
Polycarbonate (8, 9)	5–15	5–10			15	15	$1/32$		400–500 fpm
Polypropylene (10)	0–5	20–25			10	20–25			50–65 fpm
Polystyrene (11, 12)	–2	12	20	10	0–15	10	$3/16$	2 degrees above centerline	200–500 fpm
Teflon, FEP, TFE (13)	0–15		$1/2$–10						500–700 fpm
Thermosetting (14)	0					10–20			

* Although tool angles are generally similar, to obtain best results, it is advisable to follow the above recommendations.
Key—a: back rake; *b*: front clearance; *c*: end cutting edge angle; *d*: side cutting angle; *e*: side rake; *f*: side clearance; *g*: radius of cutting tip; *h*: location of tool.

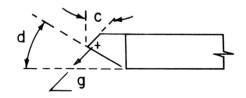

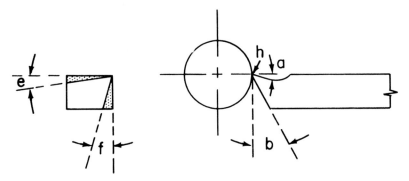

Figure 29. General purpose lathe turning tool. Letters refer to angle dimensions given in Table 46. (a) *Back rake.* For thermoplastics, less frictional heat is generated with a positive back rake, since the tool is cutting rather than scraping. (b) *Front clearance.* The angle is not critical but must be large enough to allow the tool heel to clear the piece being machined. (c) *End cutting edge.* Serves to bring the tool nose into contact with the work and to provide clearance. (d) *Side cutting.* For a given rate of feed, thinner chips result. (e) *Side rake.* Aids in the removal of plastic curls. (f) *Side clearance.* Minimizes frictional heat. (g) *Cutting tip radius.* As this increases, frictional heat may also increase. (h) *Location of tool.* Proper location of the tool prevents the piece being machined from climbing or chattering. Turning speeds and cutting angles vary with the particular plastic being used. Table 46 outlines the cutting speeds and tool angles recommended for various plastics. High speed and a fine consistent feed produce the best finish; uneven feed or dull or nicked turning tools produce a rough and irregular finish.

Milling

Milling of plastic is similar to milling of brass; however, the operator must occasionally resort to ingenious clamping arrangements, such as rubber pads, tape, etcetera, to provide adequate support of the relatively soft and flexible work piece.

(*See* turning, Chap. VI.) Spiral cutters are satisfactory except for end mill cuts. These should be made with single fluted mill cutters which provide greater chip clearance and less frictional heat.

Most thermoplastics can be milled at 350 to 750 fpm with high speed steel tools and an 0.005 to 0.010 inches feed. Table travel should be carefully controlled, since excessive speed generates a rough finish, while slow speed causes undue frictional heat.

Examples of cutting speeds for three materials follow:

Polycarbonate—425 rpm and a feed of 22 ipm or, as an alternate, 2100 rpm and a feed of 30 ipm (8, 9).

Polyamide (nylon)—1000 fpm and a feed of 9 ipm (6).

Polypropylene—400 to 500 fpm and a maximum depth of cut of 0.010 inch (10).

Sawing

The clogging of blade teeth and the excessive generation of heat are two major obstacles to sawing plastic. Both conditions produce gumming and induce stress. Jig saw and band saw blades need more set than those used for cutting steel, thereby giving clearance to the back of the blade; while circular saw blades should be slotted and hollow ground. Of the three, the band saw dissipates the greatest amount of heat. Recommended practice for several specific conditions which can serve as a guide to others are as follows:

Polycarbonate. Circular saw blades require "square and advance" teeth; whereas band saw blades require "skip teeth" (that is, 2, 3, 4 and 6 teeth/inch). Speeds should be in the range of 2300 to 5000 rpm (8, 9).

Polyamide (*nylon*). Nylon is best sawed with a "claw" tooth band saw blade of 10 teeth/inch at a speed of 400 to 5000 fpm. Circular saw blades generate heat and are not generally satisfactory (6).

Polyphenylene oxide. Use of a band saw blade with 10 to 15 teeth/inch (7).

Acrylonitrile butadiene styrene (*ABS*). Cut ABS on a band saw having a regular or wavy set blade and 4 to 14 teeth/inch. Speeds should be approximately 900 fpm. Circular saws can be used if the blade is 8 to 10 inches in diameter and has 4 to 7 teeth/inch (2).

Polystyrene. Extreme care in sawing polystyrene is critical because of its low melting temperature. Use a skip tooth band saw blade of 3 to 4 teeth/inch at a speed of 500 to 3000 fpm. The higher speeds give a smoother cut. Circular blades should be $\frac{1}{16}$ inch thick and of 6 to 8 inches in diameter, with 3 to 4 teeth/inch. Operating speed should be 2000 rpm (12).

Thermosetting plastic. An average sawing speed of 4500 fpm is effective for most reinforced and unreinforced thermosetting plastics. Saw blades should have 6 to 10 teeth/inch (10). Regardless of the type of blade used, cutting surfaces must be kept sharp at all times.

Finishing

Finishing consists of grinding, filing, sanding and buffing operations intended to impart a satisfactory degree of surface smoothness to a machined part. Such operations remove course and uneven tool marks through a progression of increasingly finer cuts and buffs. Although grinding, filing and sanding are seldom necessary for well-machined pieces, difficult shapes must at times be hand worked or repaired. Buffing, which consists of ashing, polishing, and wiping, is often required to give an ultrasmooth surface; avoid embedding grit into proposed implants.

Grinding

To determine grinding speeds for each material, practice on a piece of scrap similar in shape. Start at 4500 fpm and adjust speed, feed rate and pressure until the desired finish or surface removal rate is satisfactory. *Caution:* Avoid overheating! Coolants are essential while grinding to prevent temperature buildup.

Filing

File strokes should be long and sweeping, with light pressure. For plastics, such as acetal, nylon and polycarbonate, use a mill file having deep, single cut, coarse, curved teeth. This very sharp file produces a shaving action for smooth, clean cuts. For heat sensitive materials, use a file with rounded U-shaped grooves to prevent clogging; this is especially true for polystyrene.

Sanding

When sanding thermoplastics, use sanding grits systematically for the best finish in the shortest period of time. Start with wet sandpaper (320 grade or finer) to remove the scratch or defect. Wrap the abrasive around a soft block of rubber or felt, then rub the plastic surface, using a wide, circular motion. Keep the area well lubricated with water and use light pressure to prevent clogging. Continue the operation with increasingly finer sandpaper (for example, through 500 or 600 grade), being careful to flush residual grit from surfaces between each change.

Thermosetting materials may require the use of a coarser grit, at first, because of their harder surfaces, but the procedure is the same as for thermoplastics.

Ashing

Ashing is a buffing operation in which wet pumice is used to smooth thermoplastics. (Dentists prefer it for finishing acrylic dentures.) Buffs are 4 to 12 inches in diameter and loosely packed. Wheel speed should be 4000 fpm with No. 00 to No. 1 grade pumice. Use a hooded wheel to collect splatterings. Wash all pumice from the surface, prior to polishing. As with other machine operations, avoid overheating; otherwise minute particles of grit could become imbedded and cause irritation should the device be implanted in the body.

Polishing

Polishing of plastics requires the use of large diameter, soft, loose buffs with a fine abrasive compound, such as tripoli. Speeds of 1200 and 3000 rpm, with 12- to 16-inch diameter wheels of 4- to 5-inch width produce good results. A light touch, correct speeds and frequent rotation of the article are necessary to prevent excessive frictional heating. Wash off all traces of the polishing compound prior to the final wiping operation.

Wiping

This is the last step in imparting the final luster to a plastic piece which has been machined. A clean, soft buff, made from flannel, operated at 1200 fpm or less, suffices. Smooth, bright surfaces can be obtained by moving the object continuously under light pressure against the wheel.

ANNEALING

Annealing is the process of relieving stresses in plastic tubing, rods and sheets, induced by the manufacturing process or machining. Failure to anneal can cause cracks, crazing and dimensional changes to occur, especially when the plastic is subjected to moisture or solvent environments and mechanical loading. Crazing is readily visible, appearing as surface clouding, either locally situated or generally distributed throughout the plastic, depending upon the conditions which induced the stress. Other stresses which are not visible can reduce the functional life through flex-fatigue or loss of load bearing capabilities.

Three methods of annealing are available: (a) infrared lamps, (b) air-circulating oven and (c) immersion in a hot water or oil bath. Regardless of the method used, the polymer must be heated to a temperature approaching its heat distortion range and then gradually cooled to room temperature. Method (a) is not recommended unless the part is too large to fit into a conventional oven. Method (b) is convenient but removes surface stress only, unless extended periods of annealing are provided. Method (c) most expeditiously relieves stress throughout the bulk of the part. Temperatures must be carefully controlled to avoid subjecting the material to localized hot spots or general overheating. Optimum annealing temperatures are approximately 10 F below the minimum temperature at which the part

TABLE 47

SUGGESTED ANNEALING SCHEDULES *

Material	*Temp. (F)*	*Annealing Time*		*Ref.*
		Hrs.	*Min.*	
Acetal	212		6 to 30	(3)
Acrylic	176	10 to 22		(4)
Kel-F	302			(5)
Nylon	302		15 per ⅛″ thickness	(6)
Phenolics	248	4		
	220	24		(14)
Polycarbonate	248–266		30 to 45	(8)
Polystyrene	140	16 to 24		(12)
Teflon: FEP	500	1 per 1″ thickness		
TFE	624	1 per 1″ thickness		(13)

* Dependent upon variations in thickness, chemical type and molecular weight of the plastic. Refer to manufacturer for specific recommendations.

shows deformation of 1 percent. Table 47 suggests annealing schedules; Table 48, heat distortion temperatures.

The cooling cycle is equally as important as the heating cycle; slower rates should be used for thick sections than for thin. Accelerated cooling can induce new thermal stresses in

TABLE 48

HEAT DISTORTION TEMPERATURES OF VARIOUS POLYMERS (15)

Polymer	*Heat Distortion Temp. (F at 66 psi *)*
ABS, high impact	210–255
Acetal	338
Acrylics: cast	165–235
molded	175–225
Chlorinated polyether	285
Epoxy, cast, no filler	180–280
Flurocarbons:	
TFE	250
FEP	158
Polyvinylidene fluoride	300
Nylon 6/6	220
Phenylene oxide	280–310
Polycarbonate	270–290
Polyethylene:	
low density	100–121
medium density	120–165
high density	140–190
Polypropylene	200–250
Polystyrene	180–230
Polyvinyl chloride, rigid	135–180

* Melting temperature can be considerably higher.

the surface of the material, thereby defeating the purpose of the procedure.

FASTENING METHODS

Through holes with nuts and screws are most frequently used for fastening plastic. Other means of joining parts include the use of self-tapping screws, inserts and cements.

Though widely used, *self-tapping screws* are not recommended for plastic because of weaknesses which develop when the thread is formed. This is especially so if disassembly is likely, since repeated insertions will cut additional threads and thereby reduce the torque retention and undermine the structure. Furthermore, many threads are stripped during installation because the relative softness of plastic, as compared with metal, does not offer the resistance usually expected when a screw is tightened.

Inserts are preferred when repeated removal and insertion of screws are anticipated. Three widely used inserts are (a) the helical coil (Fig. 30), (b) the expandable and (c) the self-cutting.

The helical coil is preferred to all other inserts because it eliminates stress concentration and distributes the fastener load over a large area. It is installed either with a hot tool, which melts the plastic at the wall surface of the hole and causes it to flow into the spaces of the spring-shaped insert, or by threading the insert into a pretapped hole. The minimum material wall thickness allowable is 0.8 times the outer radius (8).

The expandable insert is used in a predrilled hole and is expanded and locked against the wall upon insertion of the screw. Material thickness around the insert should not be less than 0.9 times the final outer radius of the insert.

The self-cutting insert differs from the expandable in that it possesses external threads; however, the same criteria hold for material thickness. The hole diameter should be less than the pitch diameter, yet greater than the root diameter of the

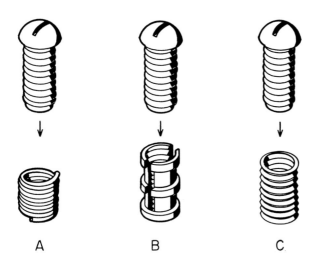

Figure 30. Typical inserts: (A) *Helical coil insert,* screws into specially tapped thread. (B) *Expansion insert,* force sets screw firmly in place. (C) *Self-cutting inserts* are similar to B, except for method of anchorage.

external threads to provide a large surface area and cross section for maximum holding strength.

Convenient tools are available from their manufacturers for applying these inserts.

New plastics are constantly appearing on the market in an effort to increase engineering design capabilities; each material will require its own set of machining conditions. This chapter can provide a basis for establishing these criteria or can be used as a general guide until such time as definitive data is established (16).

REFERENCES

1. Kobayashi, A.: *Machining of Plastics.* New York, McGraw-Hill, 1967.
2. *Machining of Cycolac Brand ABS.* Borg-Warner Technical Bulletin PB-128. Marbon Div., Borg-Warner, Washington, W.Va.
3. *Delrin Acetal Resin Post Molding Operations Bulletin.* 1963, E.I. du Pont de Nemours & Co., Inc., Wilmington, Delaware.

4. *Rohm & Haas Plexiglas Design and Fabrication Data*. Philadelphia, Rohm & Haas, 1949.
5. *Kel-F 81 Brand Plastic*. Technical Information Sheet, *Finishing-1*, 1961, Minnesota Mining and Manufacturing Co., St. Paul, Minn.
6. *Zytel Nylon Resin Machining*. Du Pont Information Bulletin No. X-47d. E.I. du Pont de Nemours Co., Inc., Wilmington, Delaware.
7. *Noryl Thermoplastic Resin Bulletin*. Polymer Products Operation, General Electric Co., Pittsfield, Mass.
8. *Lexan Polycarbonate Resins*. Fabrication Data Sheet # B 11 ff and C-10, Chemical Materials Dept., General Electric Co., Pittsfield, Mass.
9. Christopher, W.F., and Fox, D.W.: *Polycarbonates*. New York, Rheinhold Publishing Company, 1962.
10. Modern Plastics: *Modern Plastics Encyclopedia*. New York, McGraw-Hill, 1968.
11. *Machining and Finishing*. Enjay Fact Sheet #III JL. Enjay Chemical Co., 60 West 49th St., New York, N.Y.
12. *Dow Styron Bulletin: Machining and Mechanical Finishing*. The Dow Chemical Co., Midland, Michigan.
13. *Journal of Teflon®*. Reprint No. 11, E.I. du Pont de Nemours & Co., Inc., Wilmington, Delaware.
14. Society of the Plastics Industry, Inc.: *Plastics Engineering Handbook*. New York, Rheinhold Publishing Company, 1960.
15. *Modern Plastics Encyclopedia*. 1971–1972, Vol 48, No. 10A, Oct. 1971, McGraw-Hill, New York.
16. Portions of this chapter are taken from Boretos, J.W.: Machining of Plastics. In *Medical Engineering*, edited by C. Ray. Chicago, Medical Year Book Publisher.

VII

Cleaning and Sterilizing

MAJOR DIFFERENCES exist between cleaning, an essential pretreatment that must remove all foreign matter, and sterilizing, a necessary operation of killing harmful organisms which induce inflammation and rejection.

CLEANING

Surfaces must, as a first step, be sanitized of all foreign material using only cleaning agents which are known to be passive to the polymer. Thermoplastics, thermosetting resins and rubber can be cleaned with nonabrasive soap or detergent and water. Dislodge dirt with the bare hands or a soft cloth and rinse with copious amounts of water. Avoid cleaning solutions containing acetone, benzene, xylene, carbon tetrachloride, lacquer thinner or window sprays, as these often generate swelling, dissolution, softening, surface crazing and crystallization. When machining plastics, coolant solutions, other than water, water mist or air, should be eliminated. Water insoluble mold releases, which might transfer onto the surfaces of molded rubber or plastic items, must also be avoided.

Sponges and multifiber cloth are extremely difficult to clean and entail repeated washing and squeezing to free blind cells of debris. Because of its porous nature, Teflon is particularly difficult to clean. Pate (1) has associated foreign body reactions and the presence of giant cells to dirty knitted Teflon implants.

Disinfection of plastic surfaces is usually carried out by soaking the material in room temperature solutions such as chlorine quarternary ammonium salt or cationic-anionic soap solutions for ten to thirty minutes at room temperature. Boiling the object in water for five minutes or subjecting it to streaming steam are effective to the extent of killing most bacteria, except fungus spores.

Once a device is clean, it should be protected from further contamination. Assembly work should be performed in specially prepared areas having filtered air circulation. Personnel should be garbed in lint-free apparel, particularly around the head, hands and arms. Conditions enabling static electrical build-up and discharge should be prevented.

STERILIZATION

Sterilization is a step beyond cleaning; the destruction of microbial life. Bacteria or fungal spores, if present, would invade the body and cause inflammation, infection and rejection.

To achieve sterility requires special attention. Five commonly employed methods are sporicides, dry heat, gas, irradiation and steam autoclaving.

Sporicide Solution Sterilization

Although solution sterilization is convenient for many surgical tools of simple shape, the method is, nevertheless, difficult to use with good assurance when treating prosthetic implants having narrow cavities, blind holes or nonwetting surfaces. The usual procedure is to soak the object at room temperature in a sporicide such as 8% formaldehyde, 70% isopropyl alcohol or gluteraldehyde for three or more hours (2) followed by flushing with sterile, normal saline solution.

Most polymers will take on sterilizing solutions and detergents within their bulk through sorption processes. Materials with high sorption capabilities should definitely not be sterilized in this manner. For others, individual procedures should be developed to assure complete removal of the sorbed *sporicide*. Table 49 compares the sorption and transmission of water through polymers and can serve as a guide to indicate possible degrees of invasion by other liquids.

TABLE 49

SORPTION AND TRANSMISSION OF WATER IN POLYMERS (3)

Polymers	Water, Sorption *	Transmission Rate †
Polyisoprene rubber	A	D
Polyethylene (density 0.92)	A	B
Polypropylene	A	A
Polyvinyl chloride	A	B
Polyvinylidene chloride (Saran)	B	A
Polytrifluorochloroethylene (Kel-F)	A	A
Polytetrafluoroethylene (Teflon)	O	A
Polyvinyl alcohol	E	D–E
Polystyrene	C	C
Polymethyl methacrylate	A	E
Polyamide (nylon 6)	C–D	B
Polyamide (nylon ⅚)	C	C
Polyethylene terephthalate (Mylar)	A–C	B
Silicone rubber	A	E
Cellophane	E	E
Cellulose acetate	C	C

* Based on percent water sorption, 24 hour immersion, ⅛ inch‚thick sample.
Letters denote approximate range.
Key: A = 0.005 to 0.5, B = 0.6 to 1.5, C = 1.6 to 3.0,
    D = 3.1 to 5.5, E = greater than 5.6 percent.
† Based on g/m²/24 hr/mil @ 40 C. (Approximate range)
Key: A = 1.5 to 8.7, B = 28 to 126, C = 133 to 220,
    D = 240 to 400, E = 500 to 2000.

Only polyethylene, polypropylene and the fluorocarbon polymers are sufficiently hydrophobic to encourage sterilization using this method. Prolonged and vigorous rinsing techniques, however, are necessary to thoroughly flush the sporicide from these water repelling surfaces (3).

Dry Heat Sterilization

This method kills microbes by oxidation through exposure to circulating hot air. The recommended practice is based on the time and temperature relationships required to inactivate spore cultures. The following are suggested schedules: 320 F for 45 minutes, 338 F for 18 minutes, 356 F for 7½ minutes, and 374 F for 1½ minutes (4), or 572 F for 30 minutes (5). Timing should begin after the object has reached equilibrium with the oven.

Gas Sterilization

Most polymers are somewhat absorptive to gases as well as liquids. Rubber and plastic absorb and hold sterilizing gases in varying concentrations for extended periods of time. Unless special precautions are observed, tissue reactions will ensue. Ethylene oxide is one of the more convenient and commonly used gases because of its ability to kill living organisms. Unfortunately, this gas acts as a solvent for polymethyl methacrylate and will attack the plasticizers in many flexible medical tubings (6).

Rendell-Baker and Roberts (7) have recently pointed out the following essential hazards of ethylene oxide sterilization:

1. Foreign material or bacteria may remain on objects because of inadequate prior cleaning.
2. Sterilization may be incomplete because of inappropriate wrappings.
3. Residues of ethylene oxide itself, or some by-product such as ethylene glycol or ethylene chlorohydrin, may persist in the sterilized item in significant quantities at the time of use.

Bartak and Kulkarni (8) showed that simple aeration of rubber catheters was not sufficient to "degas" residual amounts of ethylene oxide. No residual gas could be detected using gas-liquid chromatography, however, after the rubber was degassed and then soaked in water for three days.

Yasuda and coworkers (3) described the amount of sorption which takes place with various plastics and the time necessary to eliminate the dissolved gas using a vacuum aerator. (*See* Table 50.)

TABLE 50

MINIMUM EVACUATION TIME OF VARIOUS POLYMERS AFTER
GAS STERILIZATION (3)

Polymers	Minimum Evacuation Time in Minutes * Thickness of Material		
	0.1 mm	*0.2 mm*	*0.3 mm*
Silicone rubber	1	4	9
Natural rubber	4	16	36
Polyurethane	25	100	225
Polyethylene	10	40	90
Polymethyl methacrylate	Time exposed to gas		
Polyethylene terephthalate (Mylar)	Time exposed to gas		
Polyamide (nylon)	Time exposed to gas		

* Based on the time the sorption reaches equilibrium value which may be considered as an estimate of the minimum time for the desorption at vacuum of less than 10^{-3} mm Hg pressure.

The following guidelines, therefore, should be observed:

1. Adsorptive materials, such as polyvinyl chloride and rubber, should be thoroughly "outgassed" following sterilization.

2. Polyethylene (3 to 5 ml thickness) and paper wrap are the best protective coverings because of their high permeability to ethylene oxide.

3. Polyvinyl chloride objects which have been gamma irradiated should not be resterilized with ethylene oxide, since significant amounts of ethylene chlorohydrin will be formed.

4. Items marked "disposable" should be discarded to prevent possible production of ethylene chlorohydrin when resterilized.

5. Water droplets should be removed from material to prevent the formation of ethylene glycol.

6. Biological indicators should be used to verify the effectiveness of sterilization.

7. Accelerated "outgassing" can be achieved by using a properly designed aerator. Each type of material must be carefully studied, however, in establishing the time reduction.

Irradiation

Gamma rays emitting from cobalt 60 radioisotope or from high voltage accelerators provide an effective means of sterilizing. This method, in particular, lends itself to prepackaged disposable items of surgery. Some material can be polymerized, cross-linked or otherwise altered by irradiation dosages. Radiation improperly employed can cause discoloration and embrittlement.

Steam Autoclaving

This is the method preferred by most surgeons for aseptic assurance. Lower temperatures and shorter exposure times are required than with dry heat sterilization. The most acceptable schedule for this treatment is 249 F for 15 minutes although 257 F for 10 minutes and 275 F for 3 minutes are acceptable

(4). Care should be exercised in selecting the exact autoclaving schedule based on the polymers ability to resist heat; for example, the lower temperature of 249 F for 10 to 15 minutes is preferred for surgeons gloves. Reference to tables giving heat distortion temperatures for each plastic will avoid inadvertent dimensional alterations. (*See* Table 48, Ch. VI.) Silicone rubber can be autoclaved repeatedly with excellent results; sterilizing by means of cold solutions, however, is not recommended because of absorption factors (9).

REFERENCES

1. Pate, J.W.: Dirty Teflon. *Am J Surg, 108:*435–436, 1964.
2. Lee, H., and Neville, K.: *Handbook of Biomedical Plastics.* Pasadena, Pasadena Tech Press, 1971.
3. Yasuda, H. Refojo, M.F., and Stone, W., Jr.: Sterilization of polymers. *Trans Am Chem Soc,* September 1964, pp. 209–215.
4. Plester, D.W.: The effects of sterilizing processes on plastics. *Biomed Eng,* September 1970, pp. 443–447.
5. Perkins, J.J.: *Principles and Methods of Sterilization.* Springfield, Charles C Thomas, 1963.
6. O'Leary, R.K., and Guess, W.L.: The toxicogenic potential of medical plastics sterilized with ethylene oxide vapors. *J Biomed Mater Res, 2:*297–311, 1968.
7. Rendell-Baker, L., and Roberts, R.B.: Gas vs. steam sterilization: When to use which. *Med Surg Rev,* 4th quarter, 1969.
8. Bartak, D., and Kulkarni, R.K.: Determination of Ethylene Oxide in Sterilized Catheters by Gas-Liquid Chromatography. Tech Report 6704, Walter Reed Medical Center, Washington, D.C., 1967.
9. Braley, S.: Personal communication.

VIII

Numerous polymer variations are used in surgical implants, blood conduits and other biomedical devices. A careful description of the polymer under investigation can minimize conflicts in performance. For example, listing the generic name of a specific material would not necessarily indicate differences in crystallinity, molecular weight, chain branching, cross-linking or end groups that could exist from batch to batch or from manufacturer to manufacturer. Difficulties in reproducing results from the work of others may stem from these unrecognized differences. Though attributing success or failure to materials described only by generic names has long been recognized as misleading (1), the practice continues. Further, undefined methods of handling polymers, inadequate analyses of the tissue pathology surrounding implants and lack of standard *in vivo* and *in vitro* test protocols add to the confusion. Also, the occasional publication of toxicological data in which only code names appear deprives the scientific community of potentially valuable data.

A description of commercial polymers should include at least the following:

1. Generic name (for example, polyethylene, polytetrafluoroethylene, silicone rubber).
2. Trade name and number (for example, Hyfax® 1900, Teflon® TFE, Medical Silastic® 382).
3. Lot or batch number.
4. Treatment (for example, method of fabrication, sterilization).

Polymers under development or chemical modification need further identification, such as

5. Source (for example, investigator, institution).
6. Composition (for example, basic formula, additives).
7. Physical state (for example, solid, amorphous).
8. Tissue pathology (if available).

Objective, careful and precise evaluation of experimental results is of paramount importance for quality control. Polymers may adversely effect the tissues or the polymer may be degraded by the host. The effect of the implant on tissues may be determined through gross observations, microscopic examination, systemic toxicology and evaluation of biological compatibility. Gross observations involve detection of alterations in tissue color, nodular or cystic changes, exaggerated development of vascular channels, suppuration, infection and necrosis. Microscopic examination discloses inflammatory reactions and degenerative changes brought on by lytic processes. Fibrous capsules around the implant should neither be excessively thick nor reveal evidence of neoplasia. Systemic toxicity can be observed through subcutaneous and intramuscular tests, especially in the sacrospinalis muscle area (2). Tissue response to the implant may be scarcely discernible or it may possess degrees of cellular and vascular involvement leading to a frank inflammation. In addition, a thorough investigation would include hematological, urological, biochemical, histopathological, allergenic and possibly carcinogenic studies.

Definitive methods for categorizing blood compatibility have not been established. "Vena caval rings" are often placed in the inferior vena cava of dogs to indicate relative thrombogenicity of materials (3). (*See* special materials, Ch. I.) The Lee-White test has been used to record time required for blood to clot *in vitro* (4). Both tests, however, are only qualitative and may not correlate well with success of a material in a particular design configuration.

Standardized test methods provide valuable information regarding long-term performance of implanted materials as influenced by its host. For example, measurements of modulus of elasticity, tensile strength, ultimate elongation, flexural strength and wear resistance are key indicators of mechanical performance capabilities. Contact angle, surface-free energy, hydrophobic, hydrophilic and oliophilic characteristics are useful in describing the surfaces of polymers and may suggest *in vivo* behavior. Many specifications for testing physical and chemical properties of materials have been established and new ones are constantly being considered (5).

Culp and co-workers (6) have outlined methods which they have found valuable for testing the physical and chemical character of biomaterials used as implants. They suggest the use of the following standards as guides:

1. ASTM D1708–59T, tensile properties of plastics by use of microtensile specimens.
2. Hardness by the indentation method per ASTM D1706–61.
3. ASTM D543–65, microscopic method of index of refraction measurement.
4. Surface irregularities by microscopic examination of wax impressions of transparent materials. The scanning beam electron microscope for deep and complex surface irregularities (using 200x–500x).
5. Creep or stress relaxation by ASTM D674–56 modified for half-size microtensile specimens.

The effect of the tissues on the implant is determined in numerous ways, based on possible changes in properties following exposure. Tests for changes in basic properties commonly employed are density determinations, differential thermal analysis, gel permeation chromatography, gradient elution, infrared spectroscopy, specific viscosity, melt index-melt viscometry, molecular weight distribution, microwave adsorption, nuclear magnetic resonance, osmometry, sedimentation method, swelling measurements and x-ray diffraction.

Also, optical properties can be evaluated by observing color, light transmission and refractive index. Changes in mechanical properties can be discerned by comparing differences in compression, dynamic, viscoelastic, flexural and tensile properties, abrasion, friction, hardness, impact resistance, stress relaxation, tear strength, torsional and wear characteristics. Further, chemical property alterations can be examined by measuring decomposition, melting and softening temperatures, extent of extractability and glass transition points. Electrical property variations can be detected by testing dielectric constant and volume resistivity.

The following groups publish specifications covering testing of plastics and rubber:

1. American Association of Textile Chemists and Colorists
   Lowell Technical Institute
   Box 28, Lowell, Mass. 01853
2. American Standards Association, Incorporated
   10 East 40th Street, New York, New York 10016
3. American Society for Testing and Materials
   1916 Race Street, Philadelphia, Pennsylvania 19103
4. The Society of the Plastics Industry, Incorporated
   Epoxy Resin Formulators Division
   250 Park Avenue, New York, New York 10017
5. Specification Activity
   Printed Materials Supply Division
   Bldg. 197, Naval Weapons Plant, Washington, D.C. 20407
6. Commanding Officer, Naval Supply Depot
   5801 Tabor Avenue, Philadelphia, Pennsylvania 19120
7. National Electrical Manufacturing Association
   155 East 44th Street, New York, New York 10017
8. U.S. Bureau of Mines
   C between 18th and 19th Streets, N.W., Washington, D.C.

A complete listing of all of these standards has been compiled by Beach (7).

To aid in the identification of polymeric materials, Table 51 is compiled from two sources (8) to provide simple tests which are indicative of each individual material. A few general observations, such as the following, performed in advance can shortcut the testing procedure:

1. Is the material thermoplastic or thermosetting. (Does it melt?)
2. Is the material rigid or extendable.

TABLE 51

SIMPLE IDENTIFICATION TESTS FOR PLASTICS (8)

Polymer	General Characteristic	Solvent	Odor On Burning	Appearance On Burning	Remarks
Thermoplastics:					
ABS	Tough, hard, rigid	Ketones	Acrid	Yellow-blue flame, black smoke	Not self-extinguishing, sharp folds display mother-of-pearl pattern
Acetals	Rigid	Solvent resistant	Formaldehyde	Blue flame, drips, no smoke	Remains rigid in boiling water, autoclavable
Acrylics	Rigid, clear	Methylene chloride, chloroform, acetic acid	Fruity	Blue flame with yellow tip	Optically clear
Cellulose acetate	Poor extensibility, tough	Acetone, alkalis, strong acids	Vinegar	Yellow flame	Optically clear
Cellulose acetate butyrate	Horn-like	Ketones, lactates	Rancid butter	Blue flame with yellow tip	Flame may spark, melt, and drip, drippings may burn
Cellulose nitrate	Very tough	Acetone, esters	Camphor	Intense white flame	Burns rapidly
Cellophane	Crumples easily, dry paper feel	Schweitzer's Reagent	Burnt paper	Burns like paper	Non-waterproof grades soften in water
Chlorinated polyether	Hard		Non-descript	Green flame with yellow tip, black smoke and soot	Self-extinguishing, flames turns greener on insertion of copper wire, autoclavable
Ethylene vinyl acetate	Tough, flexible waxy	Trichloroethylene	Acrid, sour	Orange flame with blue edges, sputters, drips	
Fluorocarbons:					
PTFE	Waxy feel	Organic amine, alkali metals	Fumes may be toxic	Drips, deforms slowly	Autoclavable, flame turns green on insertion of copper wire
FEP	Waxy feel	Organic amine, alkali metals. Not as resistant as PTFE	Fumes may be toxic	Drips, deforms slowly	Flame turns green on insertion of copper wire, autoclavable

Polymer	General Characteristic	Solvent	Odor On Burning	Appearance On Burning	Remarks
CTFE	Smooth, stronger and stiffer than two above	Organic amine, alkali metals. Not as resistant as PTFE	Acetic acid	Drips, deforms slowly	Flame turns green on insertion of copper wire, autoclavable
PVF$_2$	Smooth, strong	Not as resistant as PTFE	Acetic acid	Drips, deforms slowly	Flame turns green on insertion of copper wire, autoclavable
Nylon	Opaque, hard, no taste	Formic acid, phenol	Sour burnt wool	Yellowish sooty flame, melts to form pearls	Autoclavable
Mylar	Very tough, non-tearable	Chlorophenol	Faintly sweet	Ignites, melts to form pear-shaped drops	Autoclavable, self-extinguishing
Polycarbonate	Faint blue tint	Methylene chloride	Faintly sweet, aromatic odor	Orange flame, black soot	Autoclavable
Polyethylene	Waxy	Tetraline @ 275 F, also xylene	Paraffin wax	Smokeless blue flame with yellow tip, drips	Oriented film shrinks on heating
Polyimide	Very rigid	—	—	Chars	Autoclavable
Polyphenylene oxide	Tan	Phenol	Phenol	Yellow-orange flame spurts, difficult to ignite	Autoclavable
Polypropylene	Waxy hard	Tetraline @ 275°F	Sweet	Blue flame with yellow tip, burns slowly	Resistant to repeated flexing
Polystyrene	Hard, brittle	Benzene, xylene, methy ethyl ketone	Sweet	Burns rapidly and drips, dense black smoke and soot, yellow flame	Metallic sound when dropped, sharp folds display mother-of-pearl pattern
Polysulfone	—	—	Nondescript	Orange flame, black smoke, drips	Self-extinguishing, autoclavable
Polyurethane	Tough, rubbery	Tetrahydrofuran, dimethylacetamide	Urea	Yellow flame, black smoke	Autoclavable with care

Polymer	General Characteristic	Solvent	Odor On Burning	Appearance On Burning	Remarks
Polyvinyl chloride:					
Rigid	Hard	Cyclohexane, tetrahydrofuran, methyl ethyl ketone	Sharp, acrid fumes turn Congo paper blue	Yellow flame with green spurts	Sharp folds display white fractures, flame turns green on insertion of copper wire, self-extinguishing, autoclavable with care
Flexible	Plasticized for softness, rubbery	Cyclohexane, tetrahydrofuran, methyl ethyl ketone	Sharp, acrid fumes turn Congo paper blue	Yellow flame with pearl-like drops	Autoclavable with care
Polyvinylidene chloride (Saran)	Clear or milky	Cyclohexane	Sharp acrid	Fumes turn Congo paper blue	Resists crumpling and white fractures, flame turns green on insertion of copper wire, self-extinguishing, autoclavable, dissolved solution turns black in presence of pyridine and alcoholic potassium hydroxide solution.
Thermosets:					
Epoxy	Hard, glass-like	Allyl glycidal ether, proprietary soaks	Phenol	Black smoke	Autoclavable, brittle if non-reinforced
Polyester	Hard, glass-like	Solvent combinations with extended soaks	Hydrochloric acid	Yellow flame, blue edges	Autoclavable, brittle if non-reinforced
Silicone rubber	Rubbery	Aromatic & chlorinated solvents before vulcanization, none after vulcanization	—	White smoke	Swells in xylene

REFERENCES

1. Braley, S.A.: Commentary. *Bull Dow Corning Center for Aid to Med Res,* 6:1, 1964.
2. *U.S. Pharmacopea XVII,* 17th ed., Easton (Pa.), Mack Publishing Company, 1965, pp. 902.
3. Gott, V.L., Koepke, D.E., Daggett, R.L., Zarnstroff, W., and Young, W.P.: The coating of intravascular prostheses with colloidal graphite. *Surgery, 50:*382, 1961; and Whiffen, J., Dutton, R., Young, W.O., and Gott, V.L.: Heparin application to graphite-coated intravascular prostheses. *Surgery, 56:*404, 1964.
4. Lee, R.I., and White, P.D.: Clinical study of the coagulation of blood. *Am J Med Sci, 145:*495, 1913.
5. *ASTM Book of Standards.* American Society for Testing and Materials, Philadelphia, 1966.
6. Culp, G.W., Cupples, A.L., and Lee, H.L.: The physical and chemical characterization of nonmetallic bio-engineering materials *in vivo.* 21 *ACEMB,* Nov. 9A8, 1968.
7. Beach, N.E.: Guide to Test Methods for Plastics and Related Materials. Plastics Technical Evaluation Center, Picatinny Arsenal, Dover, N.J., 1967.
8. Taken in part from *Materials in Design Engineering,* pp. 86–87, Feb. 1967, and Bird, V. *Plastics Technology,* Sept. 1963, part V, pp. 40–41.

IX

Safety

BECAUSE the biomedical prosthetics laboratory is a combination chemical facility and machine shop, it offers a serious threat to safety. Personnel are subject to hazards from fluorinated hydrocarbons, solvents, readily combustible materials, explosive peroxides, metal and wood working machinery, mechanical presses, rollers and steam equipment.

Polyvinyl chloride, polyvinyl fluoride and polytetrafluoroethylene are potentially toxic when heated during machining and molding operations. For example, the frictional heat generated during high-speed machining of Teflon, grinding parts coated with the resin, or sawing sheets of the material can exceed 394 F, and the resulting vapors, if inhaled, can cause "polymer-fume-fever," the symptoms of which are similar to influenza. Polytetrafluoroethylene has been known to produce influenza-type symptoms when vapors, produced from heating above 400 F, have been inhaled. Teflon dust, of itself, is not toxic, but tobacco contaminated by it is a source of danger while burning. Smokers should therefore wash their hands after handling Teflon and keep their tobacco in an isolated area (1).

Paisley (2) associated respiratory outbreaks in factory workers from vapours of "isocyanate and n-oxide" produced when hot soldering irons at 572 F were applied to polyurethane wire insulation during coil winding procedures. Decomposition of polyurethanes takes place between 428 and 527 F.

Cementing operations are associated with some exposure to toxic vapors. Fumes or vapors from solvents and hardeners should not be inhaled nor absorbed through the skin. Operators frequently complain of headaches, skin rash and similar symptoms when overexposed to such vapors, especially in confined areas. To minimize these conditions, all cementing should be done under an exhaust hood or at least in a well-ventilated area.

Many plastics and rubber burn readily, giving off copious amounts of fumes and smoke. Plastics are especially vulnerable to ignition when carelessly stored in the form of loose powder or granules. Fine shavings and turnings constitute a fire hazard if allowed to accumulate. This applies to all materials except the halogenated polymers, which are generally self-extinguishing.

Peroxides are valuable cross-linking agents widely used for silicone rubber, polyesters and others. Their highly reactive characteristic, however, makes them extremely hazardous since they can burn violently or explode if merely subjected to excessive frictional heat or mechanical shock.

Experience with reinforced plastics, such as fiberglass-epoxy systems, illustrates the dangers involved in indiscriminate mixing of chemicals. Accelerators and peroxides enhance the handling and curing properties of the resin but can explode if mixed together in their concentrated form (3).

Polystyrene, acrylic and phenolics, to mention a few, are brittle and easily fractured during machining and can produce flying shards which threaten the eyes. Always wear safety glasses!

Extruder, injection molding, lathe and milling machines, platen presses, rollers, etcetera, are powerful and potentially dangerous pieces of equipment. Avoid wearing loose clothing, neckties, gloves, long-sleeved shirts, bulky coats or other articles that might become caught in rapidly revolving tools. Although most equipment includes safety switches and guards, there is no substitute for caution.

Standard safety procedures must be followed at all times. When these are overlooked, serious accidents can result.

REFERENCES

1. *Teflon TFE-Fluorocarbon Resins Safety Precautions,* Du Pont Information Bulletin No. X-59C. E.I. du Pont de Nemours & Co., Inc., Wilmington, Delaware.
2. Paisley, D.P.G.: Isocyanate hazard from wire insulation: an old hazard in a new guise. *Br J Industr Med, 26:*79–81, Jan. 1969.
3. Research Report No. 11: Fire, Explosion, and Health Hazards of Organic Peroxides. American Insurance Association, 85 John St., New York City, 1966.

I. SUBJECT

ABS. An acrylonitrile butadiene styrene polymer; impact resistant.

Accelerator. A material which increases vulcanization rate; used in conjunction with a curing agent.

Acetal. A diether polymer of alkylidene glycol.

Acrylate rubber. Saturated polyesters made by the polymerization of acrylic esters.

Acrylic. A resin based on the polymerization of acrylic acid derivatives (usually polymethyl methacrylate).

Aging. Natural deterioration by oxygen, ozone, heat and light.

Anhydrides. Organic acids which have had their water removed are anhydrides and as such have higher boiling points than their corresponding acids.

Blowing. The process by which sponge rubber is formed.

Blowing agent. A chemical which decomposes when heated to form gas to create sponge rubber.

Bonding. Joining of parts by means of a cementing material.

Boring. The process of making a hole with a rotary tool. Usually associated with a lathe operation.

Boss. A knob-like projection.

Buffing. To smooth by means of sequential ashing, polishing and wiping.

Butadiene. SBR monomer used in many synthetic rubbers.

Calender. A machine used to form or coat continuous sheets of polymer. Usually equipped with three or more rolls.

Catalyst. The term applied to a cross-linking agent; incorrectly used.

Cellophane. Film produced from wood pulp by the viscose process.

Cellulose. Long chains of glucose molecules with three reactive hydroxyl groups per glucose unit.

Chlorosulfonated polyethylene. An elastomer made by substituting chlorine and sulfonyl chloride groups into polyethylene.

Compound. An uncured rubber mixture.

Crazing. Small cracks either at the surface or throughout the entire plastic layer.

Cuprammonium process. The process of dissolving cellulose in an ammonical copper solution and spinning the solution into fibers which are reconverted to cellulose by treatment with acid.

Curing. The chemical process of converting raw rubber into an elastomer.

Curing agent. Vulcanizing or cross-linking agent.

Dimensional stability. The ability of a plastic to retain its exact shape as fabricated.

Doctor roller. A roller used for applying or metering polymers in calendering or coating processes.

Durometer. (a) An instrument for measuring hardness; (b) the measure of resistance to indentation. (*See* hardness.)

Elastomer. A rubber. A material possessing pronounced elasticity and rebound.

Epichlorohydrin. Saturated, high molecular weight aliphatic polyethers with chloromethyl side chains.

Epoxy. A resin produced by the reaction of epichlorohydrin with bisphenol or by the condensation of phenol, acetone and epichlorohydrin. Widely used as an adhesive and encapsulation compound.

Feed. To supply the material to be operated upon by the machine.

Flash. Excess material forced out of mold cavity at the parting line.

Flex fatigue. The result of a material being subjected to fluctuating stresses.

Fractol A. A heavy paraffin oil. Esso Standard Oil Co., New York, New York.

Generic name. A name common to or characteristic of a whole

group or class, nonproprietary and not protected by a
patent; such as nylon.

Gutta percha. Hard substance with same chemical composition
as natural rubber but with a slight molecular structural
variation.

Hardness. Shore and Rockwell are most commonly used measures of hardness. Shore durometer A and D are determined
with a spring-loaded indentor or probe. Shore A durometer
is for rubber and semirigid plastics and measured on a relative scale of 0 to 100. For readings over 95, change to
Shore D durometer. Rockwell hardness is derived from the
net increase of a load on a round steel ball from a minimum
to a maximum load. Hardness values are given as a function
of the diameter of the ball, load and dial scale used. Scales
for polymers:

R = 0.50″ dia. ball @ 60 kg load
L = 0.25″ dia. ball @ 60 kg load
M = 0.25″ dia. ball @ 100 kg load
E = 0.125″ dia. ball @ 100 kg load

Heat distortion temperature. That temperature at which a
standard plastic test bar deflects 0.010 inch under a maximum fiber stress of 66 or 264 psi (ASTMD-648).

ipm. Inches per minute; a measure of the feed of a machine.

Isoprene. Hydrocarbon basic to natural rubber and a monomer
used in synthetic rubbers.

Izod impact test. Method for determining behavior of materials
subjected to shock loading. The specimen is supported as
a cantilever beam and is struck by a pendulum weight.
Impact strength is determined from the amount of energy
required to fracture the specimen.

Latex. An aqueous emulsion of polymer.

Mill file. Designed for smooth filing, being single cut, tapered
in width and often possessing two square cutting edges in
addition to the cutting sides.

Milling. A machine operation in which the surface of the work
is shaped by feeding it past revolving cutters. Also, the
milling of rubber and additive ingredients on a rubber mill.

Monomer. Molecule that repeats in a polymer chain.

Nylon. A polyamide resin with recurring amide groups along the polymer chain.

pbw. Parts by weight; used to designate chemical quantities.

Permeability. Ease with which a liquid or a gas can pass through a rubber or plastic film.

Phenolics. The polymer resulting from the reaction of formaldehyde and phenol.

Phenylene oxide. A polymer of 2,6-substituted phenols; valued for its chemical resistance.

phr. Parts per hundred resin. Used to signify the amount of ingredients in grams, to be added to 100 grams of a resin or polymer.

Plastic. An organic synthetic of high molecular weight, a chain of repeating monomers that are polymerized and which can be processed into a finished article through pressure and flow.

Plasticizer. An additive used to produce softening and flexibility.

Polyamide. See nylon.

Polycarbonate. A special polyester polymer made from diphenols or dihydroxy aromatic compounds.

Polyester. A resin based on acids, alcohols or glycols and unsaturated hydrocarbons.

Polyethylene. A wax-like resin produced by the polymerization of ethylene. Usually graded according to density.

Polyimide. A polymer produced by the reaction of a suitable dianhydride with a diprimary aromatic amine.

Polymer. A giant molecule built-up by repetition of small, simple chemical units of either linear, branched or interconnected chains to form a three-dimensional network.

Polymethyl 2-cyanoacrylate. See Eastman 910.

Polymethyl methacrylate. See acrylic.

Polyolefin. A class name for the polymers derived by polymerization from relatively simple olefins, particularly polyethylene and polypropylene.

Polypropylene. A resin produced by the polymerization of propylene.

Polystyrene. A brittle resin produced by the polymerization of styrene; noted for ease of injection molding.

Polytetrafluoroethylene. See Teflon.

Polyurethane. An isocyanate polymer.

Polyvinyl alcohol. A polymer produced through the hydrolysis of polyvinyl acetate.

Polyvinyl chloride. A resin produced by the polymerization of vinyl chloride monomer with peroxide catalyst. Basically a hard and horny substance which can be plasticized to varying degrees of rigidity.

Pot life. Period of time during which a reacting thermosetting plastic or rubber composition remains suitable for its intended use after mixing with a reaction initiating agent.

Pumice. A variety of volcanic glass used for polishing in its powder form.

PVC. See polyvinyl chloride.

Rake angle. The angle between the tool face and a plane parallel to the base of the tool.

Reamer. A rotating finishing tool with cutting edges for enlarging a hole.

Resin. An organic material which will flow when subjected to stress; usually has a softening or melting range.

rpm. Revolutions per minute.

RTV. Room temperature vulcanizing. A liquid silicone rubber compound that cures at room temperature.

Schweitzer's reagent. Ammoniacal solution of copper oxide.

sfpm (fpm). Surface feet per minute; a measure of cutting speed.

Silicone. A polymer of diorgano siloxane; can be a liquid, gel, rubber or resin.

Sorption. The process of taking up and holding either by adsorption or absorption.

Solvent. A substance capable of dissolving another.

Sporicide. A substance capable of killing spores on contact; differentiated from germacides which are specific to other organisms. Example—8% formaldehyde, 70% isopropyl alcohol or gluteraldehyde.

Stock. Uncured rubber.

Stress. The intensity at a point in a body of the internal forces or components of force that act on a given plane through the point.

Tap. A tool for forming an internal screw thread.

Tensile strength. The ultimate strength of a material subjected to tensile loading.

Tripoli. A tallow filled with diatomaceous earth. The diatoms are the abrasive that removes the unwanted plastic and the tallow serves to lubricate and hold the abrasive to the wheel.

Ultimate elongation. Strain at which test specimen of rubber ruptures on stretching, given in percent of original length.

Viscose process. Cellulose products made by reacting carbon bisulfide with alkali cellulose to produce a viscous orange solution of sodium cellulose xanthate called viscose.

Vulcanization. Chemical process which converts raw rubber into an elastomer.

ZDC. Zinc dibutyldithiocarbamate, a rubber vulcanization accelerator.

II. TRADE NAMES AND MANUFACTURERS *

Aclar. A monochlorotrifluorethylene polymer. Allied Chemical Corp., New York, N.Y.

Acrylamid. American Cyanamide Corp., Stanford, Conn.

Acrylate terpolymer latex. Polyscience Inc., Philadelphia, Pa.

Acrylic catalyst. Vernon-Benshoff Co., Albany, N.Y.

Alginate impression materials and dental flasks. L.D. Caulk Co., Milford, Del.

Ajicure. An aliphatic cyclic ether amine. Ajinomoto Co., New York, N.Y.

Biomer. A segmented polyether urethane. Ethnor, Division of Ethicon, Inc., Somerville, N.J.

Boil-Soft. Ransom and Randolph Co., Toledo, Ohio.

Bondaid. An epoxy adhesive kit with an etchant for bonding Teflon®. Carl H. Biggs Co., Inc., Santa Monica, Calif.

Cab-o-sil. Cabot Chem. Co., Boston, Mass.

Carbowax. Polyethylene glycols in molecular weight range of 200 to 20,000. Union Carbide Corp., New York, N.Y.

* *Editor's Note:* Reference to specific products by their trade name is solely for identification purposes. No official support or endorsement by the National Institutes of Health (DHEW) is intended or should be inferred.

Castolite. The Castolite Co., Woodstock, Illinois.

Cellulose acetate. Eastman Chemical Co., Kingsport, Tenn.

Cerro-metals. eutectic alloys of bismuth. The Cerro Sales Corp., New York, N.Y.

Chem-grip epoxy. Chemplast Inc., Wayne, N.J.

Chemically precipitated coatings. Shipley Co., Inc., Newton, Mass.

Chemlock 607. a primer for use with silicone rubber. Hughson Chemical Co., Erie, Pa.

Conductive epoxy. J. Walman & Sons, Irvington, N.J.; Emerson and Cummings, Canton, Mass.; Electrofilm Inc., Cherry Hill, N.J.; and Technical Wire Products, Cranford, N.J.

Cuprophan PT 150. J.P. Bemberg Co., Wuppertal, Germany.

Cycleweld C-6. A chemical cement for bonding nylon, Chrysler Corp., Trenton, Mich.

Cycleweld C-14. A chemical cement for bonding acetal (must be preceded by a chromic acid surface treatment). Chrysler Corp., Trenton, Mich.

Dacron. A polyester fiber. E.I. du Pont de Nemours & Co., Inc., Wilmington, Del.

Dag. A fine particle size graphite dispersion. Acheson Colloids Co., Port Huron, Mich.

Delrin. An acetal resin, E.I. du Pont de Nemours & Co., Inc., Wilmington, Del.

Devcon. An iron reinforced epoxy casting compound. Devcon Corp., Danvers, Mass.

DER 332. An epoxy resin. Dow Chemical Co., Midland, Mich.

Eastman 910. A general purpose chemical cement (2 methyl cyanoacrylate). Armstrong Cork Co., Lancaster, Pa.

Elvanol 7260. A polyvinyl alcohol. E.I. du Pont de Nemours Co., Inc., Wilmington, Del.

Elvax 260. A ethylene/vinyl acetate copolymer. E.I. du Pont de Nemours and Co., Inc., Wilmington, Del.

Epolene C. A low molecular weight polyethylene, Eastman Chemical Products, Kingsport, Tenn.

Epon epoxy resins. Shell Chemical Co., New York, N.Y.

Epoxy EA-40. An epoxy adhesive. Smooth-on Mfg. Co., Jersey City, N.J.

Epoxylite 751. A low permeability potting epoxy resin used for encapsulating pacemakers. Lee Pharmaceuticals, South El Monte, Calif.

Epoxylite 6001M. An epoxy resin. Epoxylite Corp., South El Monte Calif.

Estane. A polyester urethane. B.F. Goodrich Co., Cleveland, Ohio.

EZ-Cast 521. A vinyl plastisol. Aremco Products, Inc., Briarcliff Manor, N.Y.

Flasks, dental. See Alginate impression materials.

Gem-Bond. Applied Plastics, El Segundo, Calif.

Hydrin. Epichlorohydrin rubber. B.F. Goodrich Co., Cleveland, Ohio.

Hydron. A hydroxyethylmethacrylate polymer. National Patent Development Corp., New York, N.Y.

Hyfax 1900. An untrahigh molecular weight polyethylene used in "total-hip prostheses." Hercules Powder Co., Wilmington, Del.

Hypalon. Chlorosulfonated polyethylene elastomer. E.I. du Pont de Nemours Co., Inc., Wilmington, Del.

Hysol AC4332. A vinyl plastisol. Hysol Corp., Oleon, N.Y.

Insl-X. A varnish. Insl-X Products Corp., Yonkers, N.Y.

Ioplex 101. A polyelectrolyte of vinyl benzyltrimethylammonium chloride and styrene sulfonate. Amicon Corp., Lexington, Mass.

Ivalon. A polyvinyl alcohol sponge, only available from Unipoint Industries, High Point, N.C.

Kel-F. A monochlorotrifluorethylene polymer. Minnesota Mining and Mfg. Co., St. Paul, Minn.

Kelmar Regular. Potassium alginate impression material. Kelco Co., Chicago, Ill.

Laminac resin. American Cyanamid Corp., Stanford, Conn.

Latex mold material. B.F. Goodrich Co., Cleveland, Ohio, and Fry Plastics International, Los Angeles, Calif.

Liqmold. Fry Plastics International Inc., Los Angeles, Calif.

Lotol 6982-Y. A natural rubber latex mold material. Naugatuck Chemical Co., Naugatuck, Conn.

Luperco AC. Lucidol Div., Wallace and Tiernan, Inc., Buffalo, N.Y.

Microcel E. Calcium silicate. Johns Manville, New York, N.Y.

Mondur TD-80. A toluene diisocyanate isomer. Mobay Chemical Co., Pittsburgh, Pa.

Mylar. An ethylene terephthalate polymer. E.I. du Pont de Nemours and Co., Inc., Wilmington, Del.

Noryl. A phenylene oxide resin. General Electric Co., Pittsfield, Mass.

Orlon. An acrylic fiber. E.I. du Pont de Nemours Co., Inc., Wilmington, Del.

Parylene C. A polymer of para xylylene. Union Carbide Corp., Chicago, Ill.

Penacolite G-1124. A chemical cement for bonding nylon. Koppers Co., Pittsburgh, Pa.

Permlastic. A polysulfide impression material. Kerr Mfg. Co., Detroit, Mich.

Plastazote. An expanded polyethylene used in splints. Expanded Rubber and Plastics Ltd., Croydon, England.

Plexiglas. A polymethyl methacrylate resin. Rohm & Haas Co., Philadelphia, Pa.

Pliobond. A rubber adhesive. Goodyear Tire & Rubber Co., Akron, Ohio.

Pluronic F-68. A nonionic surface-active agent prepared by the addition of ethylene oxide to polypropylene glycol. Wyandott Chemical Corp., Wyandott, Mich.

Polyethylene CL-100. A peroxide cross-linked polyethylene used for rotomolding. Phillips Petroleum Co., Bartlesville, Okla.

Polyethylenemethacrylate. A reinforcing agent. Rohm and Haas Co., Philadelphia, Pa.

Poly-Prep. A fast, easy-to-use treatment for bonding polyethylene. Chemclean Corp., College Point, N.Y.

Polysar X-414. A trans-1,4 polyisoprene polymer. Polymer Corp. Lmtd., Sarnia, Ontario.

Polytrans. Dental Perfection Co., Glendale, Calif.

Primer A-29550. Bradley and Vroohman Co., Chicago, Ill.

PS-18 (PS-30). A chemical cement for producing bubble-free clear joints with acrylic. Cadillac Plastics, Detroit, Mich.

R149X32-1 prepolymer and R149X32-4 amine curative. A polyester polyurethane. Goodyear Tire and Rubber Co., Akron, Ohio.

Resiweld 620 and 7620. An epoxy adhesive used to encapsulate electronic pacemakers. H.B. Fuller Co., St. Paul, Minn.

Rigidax. An inorganic salt. W.S. Arguesco Co., Inc., Mamaroneck, N.Y.

Saran. A vinylidene chloride polymer. Dow Chemical Corp., Midland, Mich.

Silastic. A siloxane elastomer. Dow Corning Corp., Midland, Mich.

Silicure. RTV silicone rubber catalyst. General Electric Co., Waterford, N.Y.

Softdent. A soft liner for dentures made from Hydron. Dentomed Co., New York, N.Y.

Stafoam PE102. A foam-in-place polyurethane flexible sponge. American Latex Products Corp., Hawthorne, Calif.

Tam-mold. A liquid vinyl dispersion. Tamite Industries, Inc., Hialeah, Fla.

Teflon. Two types: FEP and TFE. FEP is a fluorinated ethylene propylene polymer. TFE is a tetrafluoroethylene polymer. E.I. du Pont de Nemours Co., Inc., Wilmington, Del.

Tetra-etch. A fast, easy-to-use treatment for bonding Teflon. W.L. Gore & Assoc., Inc., Newark, Del.

Trithene. A monochlorotrifluorethylene polymer. Union Carbide, Chicago, Ill.

Tygon. A polyvinyl chloride compound. Norton Co., Akron, Ohio.

Versamid. General Mills, Inc., Kankakee, Ill.

Visking. American Viscose Co., Fredericksburg, Va.

Vulcalock. A primer for bonding natural rubber. B.F. Goodrich Co., Cleveland, Ohio.

Vulcastab L.S. A stabilizer for natural rubber latex. R.T. Vanderbilt Rubber Co., Inc., New York, N.Y.

Note: Temperatures in Fahrenheit are used throughout this book for consistency with the industrial data represented.

Appendix

THROUGHOUT this monograph, the properties of polymers for prosthetic replacement have been discussed. To add perspective, some knowledge of the characteristics of living tissues is in order.

The physical properties of the various parts of the body, as presented in Tables 52 and 53, are only approximately similar to their living counterparts because of a number of factors.

Often, absolute values are difficult to obtain because of variations which can exist within the method of testing and tissue changes which occur immediately upon removal of a specimen. For example, muscle of the body will loose as much as 60 percent of its ultimate tensile strength (that is, a change from 25 to 70 psi to 15 to 40 psi) after twenty-four hours postmortem and influences the data from the outset.

Needless to say, a device cannot be selected on the basis of its physical similarity to living systems without considering other properties and the importance of biological interactions.

Table 52 gives the comparative physical properties of bone. It is apparent that vertebrae are considerably weaker than the bones of the arm, leg and skull; these latter three are somewhat similar in strength.

Table 53 gives the physical properties of selected soft tissues. Tendon is more resistant to tensile forces than either skin or elastic cartilage. The trachea and ureter have greater strength in the longitudinal direction whereas the vena cava and aorta are strongest in the transverse direction. Figures for the strength of most muscles of the body, for example see cardiac muscle, are surprisingly low in view of the tremendous work which they perform.

TABLE 52

COMPARATIVE PROPERTIES OF RIGID BODY TISSUES * (1)

Tissue	Description of Test	Tensile Strength (psi)	Ultimate Elongation (%)	Compressive Strength (psi †)	Modulus of Elasticity (psi × 10⁶ †)
Bones of leg:					
Femur	(a)	17,600	1.41	24,200	25.0
Tibia	(a)	20,300	1.50	23,000	26.2
Fibula	(a)	21,200	1.59	17,800	26.9
Bones of arm:					
Humerus	(a)	18,800	1.43	19,200	24.9
Radius	(a)	21,600	1.50	16,600	26.9
Ulna	(a)	21,400	1.49	17,000	26.7
Vertebra:					
Cervical	(b)	450	0.75	1,460	—
Upper thoracic	(b)	480	0.77	1,020	—
Lower thoracic	(b)	510	0.78	870	—
Lumbar	(b)	540	0.80	770	—
Skull	Tangential	3,650 (2)	—	—	—
	Radial	—	—	14,000 (2)	—
Tooth, molar crown and molar root	—	—	—	20,900	—

* All values represent averages of several wet measurements, from average adults usually 20 to 39 years of age, with average deviations of 5 to 15 percent using a Schopper or Amsler tension tester.

† The compressive strength of compact bone is greatest in persons 20 to 39 years of age and 87 percent of that for persons 60 to 69 years of age.

Key: (a) Long axis of specimen parallel to intact compact bone; 2.5 mm diameter bar with a 5:1 length to diameter ratio. (b) Smaller specimens were used by reducing the diameter used in (a).

TABLE 53

COMPARATIVE PROPERTIES OF SOFT BODY TISSUES * (1)

Tissue	Description of Test †	Tensile Strength (psi)	Ultimate Elongation (%)
Skin	(a)	1,100	78
Tendon	(b)	7,680	9.4
Elastic cartilage	(c)	440	30
Trachea	Transverse	51	81
	Longitudinal	313	61
Heart valves			
Tricuspid	Radial	140	14
	Circumferential	220	15.8
Biscuspid	Radial	260	16.0
	Circumferential	260	15.9
Pulmonary	Radial	60	22.4
	Circumferential	570	10.6
Aortic	Radial	65	15.3
	Circumferential	380	10.0
Cardiac muscle		16	63.8
Inferior Vena Cava	Transverse	440	51
	Longitudinal	170	84
Ascending aorta	Transverse	155	77
	Longitudinal	10	81
Ureter	Transverse	68	98
	Longitudinal	150	36
Muscle, Rectus Abdominus	‡	46	61

* All values represent averages of several wet measurements, from average adults usually 20 to 39 years of age, with average deviations of 5 to 15 percent using a tension tester.
† Tests: (a) Membranous organs and tissues test samples were strips 10 mm long x 2 to 3 mm wide with a 3:1 length to width ratio. (b) Tendon specimens were bundles 3 cm long with a cross-sectional area of 0.5 to 0.8 mm². (c) Cartilage specimens were cut parallel to long axis of costal cartilage, 25 mm x 10 mm x 1 mm thick.
‡ These values were taken 48 hrs postmortem when an estimated drop of 60% occurs for all muscle.

REFERENCES

1. Unless otherwise specified, data from Yamada, H.: *Strength of Biological Materials.* Baltimore, William & Wilkins Company, 1970.
2. *Head Injury Model Construction Program Data Compilation and Review.* Morgantown, West Virginia University, June 1971.

Cobey, M.D., 29, 37
Cook, G.B., 9, 35
Cooper, T., 105
Coover, H.W., Jr., 110, 121
Craig, R.G., 107
Craig, W.M., 106
Critchfield, F.H., 50
Critchfield, F.H., Jr., 47, 50
Cross, R.A., 36
Culp, G.W., 50, 147, 152
Cupples, A.L., 50, 152

D

Daggett, R.L., 38, 152
Danahy, P.R., 26, 37
Dantowitz, P., 12, 36
DeBroske, J.M.F., 106
Deibert, M.D., 36
Dental Perfection Co., 102
Dentomed Co., 21
Detmer, D.E., 28, 37, 106
Devcon Corp., 57
de Villiers, R., 49
Devine, A., 112, 121
Donachy, J.H., 106
Dootz, E.R., 100, 107
Dow Chemical Co., 30, 111
Dow Corning Corp., 11, 58, 69, 73, 103, 117
Duda, E., 121
Du Pont, i.e. Du Pont de Nemours Co., Inc., 28, 61, 94, 105
Durrer, D., 38

E

Eastman Chemical Co., 15
Edwards Laboratory, 9
Edwards, M.L., 35
Ehle, A.L., 50
Eisenberg, L., 49
El-Ebrashi, M.K., 91, 106
Electrofilm Inc., 93
Elvanol, 28, 61
Elvax 260, 48
Emerson and Cummings Inc., 93
Enger, C.C., 48, 50
Epoxylite Corp., 58
Estane, 100
Ethnor Inc., 64, 116
Expanded Rubber and Plastics Ltd., 26

F

Fairchild, J.M., 55, 105
Falb, R.D., 34, 38
Farkas, R.D., 122
Firtell, D.N., 68, 106
Foltz, E.L., 50
Foote, J.L., 106
Fox, D.W., 137
Frank, H.A., 45, 49, 50
Frank, N.R., 58, 105
French, L.A., 49
Frisch, J., 121
Fromm, E., 49
Fry, D.L., 36
Fry Plastics International Inc., 102, 103
Furuse, A., 36

G

Gaertner, R.A., 86, 106
Gage, A.A., 49
Galletti, P.M., 12, 13, 36
Gardner, D.L., 35
General Electric, 59, 69, 103
General Mills, 18, 113
Ghosh, J.C., 106
Gibson, R.I., 48, 50
Glenn, W.W.L., 49
Gonsior, L.J., 34
Goodman, A.H., 50
Goodman, R.M., 48, 50
Goodrich, i.e. B.F. Goodrich Co., 7, 10, 62, 63, 102, 115
Goodyear Tire and Rubber Co., 10, 113
Gore, i.e. W.L. Gore Associates, 114
Gott, V.L., xii, 32, 36, 38, 152
Gould, F.E., 36
Gourley, I.M.G., 17, 36
Greatbach, W., 49
Grode, G.A., 7, 32, 34, 38
Grotta, H.M., 38
Guess, W.L., 144
Guttmann, W.H., 108, 120

H

Haim, G., 122
Halprin, B.D., 33, 38
Hamilton, W.D., 106
Hancock, W.D., 35
Harvey, E., 49